Statistical Process Control

Statistical Process Control

A practical guide

John S. Oakland

Ph.D, MRSC, CChem, FIQA, FSS

Senior Lecturer in Production Management,
University of Bradford Management Centre

A HALSTED PRESS BOOK

JOHN WILEY & SONS, INC.
New York

Published in the U.S.A. by
Halsted Press, a division of
John Wiley & Sons, Inc., New York

ISBN 0–470–20360–9 (USA)

Library of Congress Cataloging in Publication Data

Printed in Great Britain

To Susan, my wife

Contents

Preface

To be successful in today's economic climate, any manufacturing organization and its suppliers must be dedicated to continuing improvements in quality. More efficient ways to manufacture goods that consistently meet the needs of the customer must be sought. There is now increasing pressure on those in the supply chains of manufacturing companies to do so.

To achieve this two things are required: senior management commitment to improvements in quality and the use of effective methods. This book sets down some of the basic principles of quality to provide a platform for the former, and addresses the requirements of the latter by describing the statistical methods used in process quality control. It covers the subject of Statistical Process Control (SPC) in a basic but comprehensive manner, with the emphasis on a practical approach throughout. A special feature is the use of real-life examples, from a number of industries.

The traditional approach of final inspection of manufactured items to sort out those not meeting specifications is rejected as a means of controlling quality. The techniques presented here are designed to prevent the production of waste by better control during the manufacturing process. This requires an understanding of elementary statistics, preferably tackled within the framework of practical production quality problems facing industry today.

The book is not written for the professional statistician or mathematician – indeed attempts have been made to eliminate much of the mathematical jargon that often causes distress. Those interested in pursuing the theoretical aspects will find references to books and papers for further study.

Where possible, procedures have been included to simplify the application of 'statistical tools' to provide powerful techniques with which to improve product quality and reduce costs. The book deals with the difference between the British and American systems of process control chart design, an area of potential confusion to all students of the subject.

The book is written to meet the requirements of students in universities, polytechnics, and technical colleges engaged in courses on science, engineering and management subjects, including quality assurance. It also serves as a textbook for self or group instruction of production and inspection supervisors, engineers, scientists, technologists, and managers. The text offers clear guidance and help to those unfamiliar with either quality control or statistical applications.

The author would like to acknowledge the contributions to improvements in methods of teaching statistical quality control, made by his colleagues Professor Keith Lockyer and Dr Roy Followell. These have made the writing of this book so much easier. He would also like to thank Ann Falkingham, Bessie Miller, and Carol Swales who have fought courageously with the manuscript and the word processor. Thanks also to my own 100 per cent inspection of the book for the errors left in it.

CHAPTER 1

The Control of Quality

1.1 Introduction

The author recalls a telephone call from a worried managing director of a medium-sized engineering firm. The M.D. was desperate for help. He explained that approximately 15% of his work force were now employed as finished product inspectors and that this had helped tremendously to reduce the number of external failures – customer complaints and warranty claims. He was left, however, with a different problem: internal failure – a huge pile of scrap material and products for rework, the sight of which preyed on his mind and kept him awake every night.

The problem was only a symptom of the real, underlying cause of this type of failure – the lack of understanding of quality management. The concentration of inspection effort at the final product stage merely shifts the failure costs from outside the company to inside. To reduce total failure costs, quality control must be at the point of manufacture: quality cannot be inspected into any item after it has been manufactured. It is essential for cost-effective control to ensure that articles are manufactured correctly the first time and the aim of process control is the prevention of the manufacture of defective products.

Since the responsibility for manufacture lies with the production department, the responsibility for achieving the appropriate quality in manufacture must also lie with production. To fulfil this responsibility production staff must be provided with the tools necessary to:

1. know whether or not they are meeting the specifications,
2. make a correct adjustment to a process which has moved 'out of control'.

Statistical quality control techniques, backed by management commitment and good organization, provide objective methods of process quality control.

The reputation attached to a company for the quality of its products is accepted as a key to its success and the future of its employees. For industrial organizations, which are viable only if they provide satisfaction to the consumer, competitiveness in quality is not only central to profitability, but crucial to business survival. The consumer is not required to make a choice between price and quality. If any manufacturing company is to continue to exist, therefore, it must learn how to manage quality. In today's tough and challenging business environment, the development and implementation of a comprehensive quality policy is not merely desirable – it is essential.

It is no exaggeration to say that process quality control is vital to the efficient conduct of affairs in any modern developed society. Many day-to-day issues, often taken for granted, involve quality control in some form or another.

For example, the safety and conformity of pharmaceuticals and food processing, the continuity of performance and safe operation of nuclear plants and off-shore installations, the effectiveness of weapons, the relative merits and life-cycle costs of competing products, and efficiency of services, all attest to the need for good control of quality.

The quality of products is important not only for users but also for suppliers. For manufacturers, quality deficiencies result in additional costs for inspection, testing, scrap, rework, and the handling of complaints. Repeat sales and future market share will also be affected, with significant effects on profitability and survival. Quality must, therefore, be taken into account throughout all the areas of design, manufacture, marketing, and purchasing. It must be controlled in all these functions, and their activities co-ordinated to achieve a balanced corporate quality performance. Quality performance will not just happen, effective leadership and teamwork is the only sure recipe for success. Understanding and commitment by senior management together with explicit quality policies lead to action throughout the entire organization, which in turn generates a momentum for quality improvement of products and performance.

Management must be dedicated to the ongoing improvement of quality, not simply a one-step improvement to an acceptable plateau. There must be willingness to implement changes, even in the ways in which an organization does business, in order to achieve that improvement. In addition, innovation and resources are required to satisfy the long-term requirements of the customer and the company, which must be placed before short-term profitability.

A traditional approach to manufacturing is to depend on production to make the product and quality control to inspect it and screen out items which do not meet specifications. This is a strategy of detection and is wasteful because it allows time and materials to be invested in products which are not always saleable. This post-production inspection is expensive, unreliable, and uneconomical.

It is much more effective to avoid waste by not producing unsaleable output in the first place – to adopt a strategy of prevention. The prevention strategy sounds sensible and obvious to most people. It is often captured in slogans such as; 'Quality – Right First Time'. This type of campaigning is, however, not enough on its own. What is required is an understanding of the elements of a systematic control system which is designed for the prevention of defective manufacture. What follows is the basis of such a system.

A quality assurance system, based on the fact that all functions share responsibility for quality, provides an effective method of acquiring and maintaining desired quality standards. The quality assurance department should not assume direct responsibility for quality but should support, advise, and audit the work of the other functions, in much the same way as a financial auditor performs his duty without assuming responsibility for the profitability of the company.

The actual control of quality during manufacture must rest squarely on the shoulders of production management, who must ensure that all the appropriate concepts and techniques are applied to this task. Organizationally, this means that staff carrying out work to control quality must be within the production function.

The control of quality is a managerial function in which the quality of raw materials, processes, and products is controlled for the purpose of preventing the release of defective goods. To meet this reponsibility, organizations must use every device practicable to prevent, detect, and correct errors that occur in the steps of manufacture. This implies that, to achieve the control of quality, the variables which may affect quality and which can result from the actions of men, the nature of materials, and the performance of machines, must all be controlled.

Technologies and market conditions vary between different industries and markets, but the basic concepts of quality management and the financial implications are of general validity. The objective should be to produce, at an acceptable cost, goods which conform to the requirements of the customer. The way to accomplish this is to use a systematic approach in the operating departments of design, manufacturing, quality assurance, purchasing, sales, and others – nobody should be exempt. The statistical approach to quality control is not a separate science or a unique theory of quality control – rather a set of valuable tools which becomes an integral part of the 'total' quality approach.

Two of the most famous authors on the subject of quality management are Drs Walter Shewhart and W. Edwards Deming. In their book, 'Statistical Method from the Viewpoint of Quality Control', is taken this quotation, 'The long-range contribution of statistics depends not so much upon getting a lot of highly trained statisticians into industry as it does on creating a statistically minded generation of physicists, chemists, engineers, and others who will in any way have a hand in developing and directing production processes of tomorrow'. This was written in 1939. It is as true today as it was then.

1.2   Design and Conformance

In manufacturing, one of the most commonly misunderstood words is 'quality'. What is a high quality pair of shoes or a high quality washing machine? It is meaningless to make statements about the degree of quality of a product without reference to its intended use or purpose. Shoes which are to be used in the performance of a ballet would obviously have different requirements to those used in mountaineering, but both pairs of shoes may have the same level of quality, i.e. they are equally suitable for the purpose for which they were manufactured.

We define quality then as 'the degree of fitness for purpose or function', indicating that it is a measure of the satisfaction of customer needs. So the quality of a motor car, or washing machine, or a pair of shoes is the extent to which it meets the requirements of the customer and, therefore, before any discussion on quality can take place it is necessary to be clear about the purpose of the product, in other words, what those customer requirements are. The customer may be within or without the organization and his/her satisfaction must be the first and most important ingredient in any plan for success.

A word of warning: the customer's perception of quality changes with time and the company's attitude to quality must, therefore, change with this perception. The skills and attitudes of the producer are also subject to change. Failure to monitor such changes will inevitably lead to dissatisfied customers. Quality, like all other corporate matters, must be continually reviewed in the light of current circumstances.

The quality of a product has two distinct but inter-related aspects:

Quality of Design, and
Quality of Conformance to Design.

Quality of Design

This is a measure of how well the product is designed to achieve its stated purpose. If the quality of design is low, the product will not work.

The most important feature of the design, with regard to the achievement of the required product quality, is the specification. This describes and defines the product and should be a comprehensive statement of all aspects of the product which must be present to meet customer requirements.

The stipulation of the correct specification is vital in the purchase of materials and components for use in manufacture. All too frequently, the terms, 'as previously supplied', or 'as agreed with your representative', are to be found on purchasing orders for bought-out items. The importance of obtaining materials of the appropriate quality cannot be over-emphasised and it cannot be achieved without adequate specifications. Published standards should be incorporated into purchasing documents wherever possible.

A specification may be expressed in terms of: the maximum amount of tolerable variation on a measurement, the degree of finish on a surface, the smoothness of movement of a mechanical device, a particular chemical property, etc. There are a variety of ways in which the specification of a product may be stated and the ingenuity of man must be constrained in order to control the number of forms of specifications present in any organization.

A question which is frequently asked in manufacturing is, 'Why are the tolerances so tight?' This raises the question of the criteria for establishing the precision of the design, which should be predominantly the in-service performance requirements of the end product. Work on tolerance specification and relative process costs has been carried out at the U.S. Army Management Engineering Training Centre in Illinois. This shows that movement towards tighter and tighter tolerances generally requires the change to processes which are more and more costly. This is represented by the curve in Fig. 1.1. which rises more and more steeply as attempts are made to further increase precision. Tolerances which are based only on 'idealistic design concepts' will result in extremely high manufacturing costs.

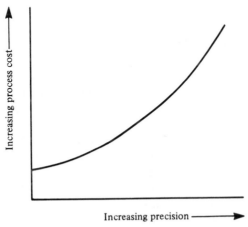

Fig. 1.1   Costs and precision of design

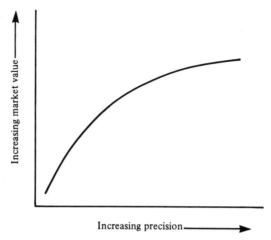

Fig. 1.2   Value and precision of design

Given this relationship between precision and manufacturing costs, it follows that it is not sensible to aim for absolute perfection. The other side of the coin is the relationship between precision and market value or price. Higher precision will inevitably demand a higher market value but, owing to the reluctance on the part of the purchaser to pay more money for effectively the same product, this value increases at a decreasing rate. This is represented by the curve of Fig. 1.2 which rises less steeply as tighter and tighter tolerances are achieved.

Figure 1.3 shows a typical value v. precision curve superimposed onto a typical cost v. precision curve for a manufactured product. The cost of trying to achieve perfection increases at an accelerating rate whilst the rate of increase in market value decelerates. The difference between the market value and the cost, the 'contribution', may be calculated and is shown as the dotted curve in Fig. 1.3. The precision level at which the contribution per article is a maximum is the point at which the market dictates a manufacturer should operate.

There must be a corporate understanding of the company's quality position in the marketplace. It is not sufficient that the marketing department specifies a quality, 'because that is what the customer wants'. There must also be an agreement that the production departments can produce to that quality. Should production be incapable of achieving the desired quality, then one of two things must happen. Either the company finds a different position in the marketplace or substantially changes the production facilities.

It is virtually impossible for a manufacturing unit to operate at more than one quality level. The concept of taking in some orders to fill up the gaps

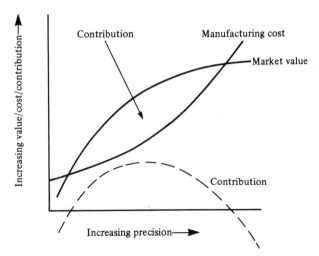

Fig. 1.3 Contribution and precision of design

with products of significantly lower quality – and assumed to be easier to make – will eventually debase all quality to the lower level.

Quality of Conformance to Design

This is the extent to which the product achieves the quality of design. What the customer actually receives should conform to the design, and manufacturing costs are tied firmly to the level of conformance achieved. Quality cannot be inspected into a product, the customer satisfaction must be designed into the production system. The conformance check then makes sure that things go according to plan.

A high level of final product inspection is often indicative of attempts to inspect in quality, an activity which will achieve nothing but spiralling costs and decreasing viability.

The area of conformance to design is concerned largely with the quality performance of the manufacturing function. The recording and analysis of data play a significant role in this aspect of quality and it is here that the tools of statistical process control must be applied effectively.

1.3 Quality Related Costs

Obtaining a product which has a high level of quality, that is a high degree of fitness for purpose, is not enough. The cost of achieving that quality must

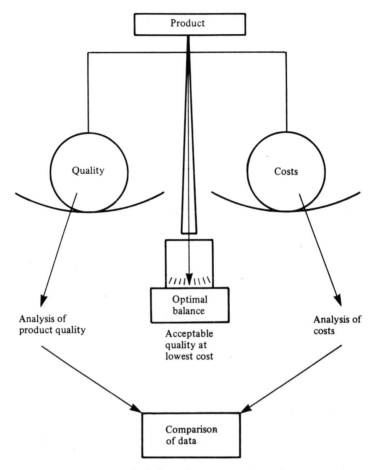

Fig. 1.4   The balance between quality and cost

be carefully managed so that the long-term effect of quality costs on the business is a desirable one. These costs are a true measure of the quality effort. A competitive product based on a balance between quality and cost factors is the principal goal of responsible production management. This objective, which is highlighted in Fig. 1.4, is best accomplished with the aid of competent analysis of the costs of quality. The balance works like this: as quality goes down, costs go up and as quality improves, costs will fall. The analysis of quality costs is a significant management tool which provides:

● A method of assessing the overall effectiveness of the management of quality.
● A means of determining problem areas and action priorities.

The costs of quality are no different to any other costs in that, like the costs of maintenance, design, sales, production, and other activities, they can be budgeted, measured, and analysed.

Having specified the quality of design, the manufacturing plant has the task of making a product which matches this quality. This comprises activities which will incur costs that may be separated into the categories of failure costs, appraisal costs, and prevention costs. Failure costs can be further split into those resulting from internal and external failure.

Internal Failure Costs

These costs occur when products fail to reach designed quality standards and are detected before transfer to the consumer takes place. Internal failure includes:

Scrap   Defective product which cannot be repaired, used or sold.
Rework or Rectification   The correction of defective material to meet the required specifications.
Re-Inspection   The re-examination of products which have been rectified.
Downgrading   Product which is usable but does not meet specifications and may be sold as 'second quality' at a low price.
Failure Analysis   The activity required to establish the causes of internal product failure.

External Failure Costs

These costs occur when products fail to reach design quality standards and are not detected until after transfer to the consumer. External failure includes:

Repair   Either of returned products or those in the field.
Warranty Claims   Failed products which are replaced under guarantee.
Complaints   All work associated with servicing of customers' complaints.
Returns   The handling and investigation of rejected products.
Liability   The result of product liability litigation and other claims.

External and internal failures produce the 'costs of getting it wrong'.

Appraisal Costs

These costs are associated with the evaluation of purchased materials, processes, intermediates and products to assure conformance with the specifications. Appraisal includes:

Inspection and Test   Of incoming material, process set-up, first-offs, running processes, intermediates and final products, and includes product performance appraisal against agreed specifications.

Quality Audits   To check that the quality system is functioning satisfactorily.

Inspection Equipment   The calibration and maintenance of equipment used in all inspection activities.

Vendor Rating   The assessment and approval of all suppliers.

Appraisal activities result in the 'costs of checking it is right'.

Prevention Costs

These are associated with the design, implementation, and maintenance of the quality system. Prevention costs are planned and are incurred prior to production. Prevention includes:

Product Requirements   The determination of quality requirements and the setting of corresponding specifications for incoming materials, processes, intermediates, and finished products.

Quality Planning   The creation of quality, reliability, production, supervision, inspection, and other special plans (e.g. pre-production trials) required to achieve the quality objective.

Quality Assurance   The creation and maintenance of the overall quality system.

Inspection Equipment   The design, development and/or purchase of equipment for use in inspection work.

Training   The development, preparation, and maintenance of quality training programmes for operators, supervisors, and managers.

Miscellaneous   Clerical, travel, supply, shipping, communications, and other general office management activities associated with quality.

Resources devoted to prevention give rise to the 'costs of making it right the first time'.

The relationship between these so-called *direct* costs of prevention, appraisal, and failure and the ability of the organization to meet the customer requirements is shown in Fig. 1.5. Where the ability to match a quality acceptable to the customer is low, the total direct quality costs are high, the failure costs predominating. As ability is improved by modest investment in prevention and possibly appraisal, the failure costs drop, initially very steeply. There will be an optimum operating level at which the combined costs are at the minimum.

So far little has been said about the often intractable indirect quality costs associated with customer dissatisfaction, and loss of reputation or goodwill. These costs reflect customer attitude towards an organization and may be

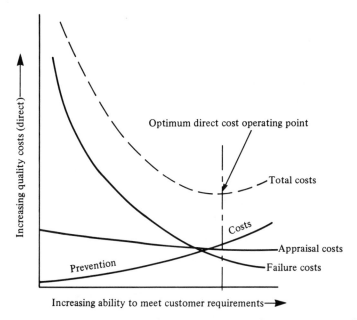

Fig. 1.5   Relationship between direct costs of quality and organization capability

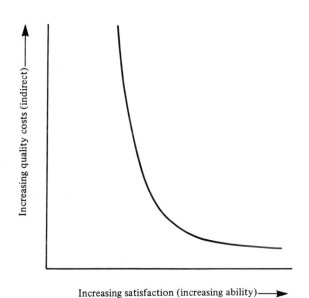

Fig. 1.6   Relationship between indirect costs of quality and customer satisfaction

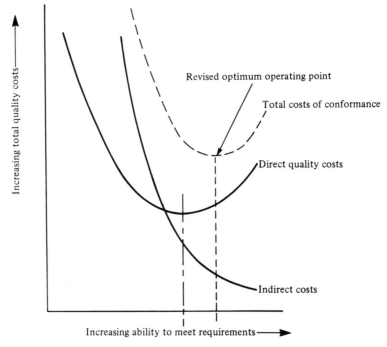

Fig. 1.7   Relationship between total costs of quality conformance and organizational ability

considerable. Figure 1.6 portrays the relationship between indirect quality costs and the organization's ability to provide customer satisfaction.

The total conformance quality costs, obtained by addition of direct and indirect quality costs (Fig. 1.7), are at a minimum when the organization's capability matches customer satisfaction. It is worthy of note that the indirect costs may move the 'optimum' point to the right indicating the need for a lower product defect level or another form of improvement in customer satisfaction. Indirect quality costs, like direct costs, may be lowered by relatively small increases in prevention – the cause of customer dissatisfaction and loss of reputation. Failure costs will never be removed completely – some after-sales service will be needed and some complaints will always be received.

Total direct quality costs, and their division between the categories of prevention, appraisal, internal failure, and external failure, vary considerably from industry to industry and from plant to plant. Juran's work, showing that total quality costs in manufacturing average 10 per cent of sales turnover, mean that in the average organization there exists a 'hidden plant' amounting to approximately one tenth of productive capacity. This is devoted to producing scrap, rework, correcting errors, replacing defective goods and so on. Thus, a direct link exists between quality and productivity and there is no better way to improve productivity than to convert this hidden plant to truly productive use. A systematic approach to the control of quality provides an important way to accomplish this.

CHAPTER 2

Quality Data and its Presentation

2.1 The Systematic Approach

If we adopt the definition of quality: 'fitness for purpose', then we have already seen that this requires the subject to be considered in terms of quality of design and quality of conformance to design. To achieve quality, therefore, will require the following:

- an appropriate design,
- suitable resources and facilities, (men, machines, and money)
- the correct materials,
- an appropriate manufacturing process,
- a set of detailed instructions.

To reach this stage, it is necessary to adopt a systematic approach in all the activities leading to it. Basically this is quite simply narrowing down each task until it is of a manageable size.

Considering the design stage, it is vital to ensure that the specification for the product is realistic. Excessive, unnecessary detail here frequently results in the specification being ignored, at least partially, under the pressures to contain costs. It must be reasonably precise and include some indication of priority areas. Otherwise it will lead to a product which is unacceptable to the market. A systematic monitoring of product performance should lead to better and more realistic specifications. That is not the same thing as adding to the volume or detail of the documents.

The 'narrowing-down' approach to problem solving in manufacturing forces attention to be focussed on one of industry's major difficulties in quality – the conformance or the ability to manufacture consistently to the design specification. This comprises the control of a number of features:

- the purchased materials,
- the manufacturing process,
- the product (or intermediate).

Consideration of the first chapter in this book suggests that control of the manufacturing process is by far the most important of these three. The quality of the purchased materials is a function of the suppliers' ability to control their processes. If all suppliers in the chain adequately control their processes, then the finished product for sale at each stage will be of the specified quality.

This is a very simple message which cannot be over stated, but some manufacturing companies still employ a large inspectorate, including many who devote their lives to sorting out the bad from the good, rather than tackling the essential problem of ensuring that the production process remains in control. The role of the 'inspector' should be to check and audit the systems of control, advise, calibrate, and where appropriate undertake complex measurements or assessments. Quality can only be controlled at the point of manufacture, it cannot be elsewhere.

In applying a systematic approach to quality control, there are two basic rules:

1. Record all the data – especially at the point of manufacture. If data is not carefully and systematically recorded, it cannot be analysed and put to good use. Information recorded in a suitable way enables the magnitude of variations and trends to be observed and analysed for errors, process capability, vendor ratings, etc. Numerical data is often not recorded, even though measurements have been taken – a simple tick is often used to indicate within specification. The requirement to record the actual numbers has a marked effect on the reliability of the data. For example, if a result is only just out of tolerance, it is tempting to put down another tick but the recording of false figures is less likely. This factor should not be under-estimated.

2. Use appropriate techniques – the essential tools of the 'narrowing-down' approach. There are available a wide range of simple, yet powerful, problem-solving and data-handling techniques which should be part of the kit. They include:

● Data gathering,
● Histograms,
● Graphs,
● Pareto analysis,
● Cause and effect analysis,
● Scatter diagrams,
● Statistical methods of process control.

2.2 Data Gathering

Data will form the basis for decisions and action and its form will obviously differ from one production process to another. Information is collected to discover the actual situation. It may be used as part of a process or product control system and it is important to know just what the data are to be used for. For example, if a problem occurs in the amount of impurity present in a product which is manufactured continuously, it is not sufficient to take only one sample per day to find out the variations between different shift operators. Similarly in comparing defects produced by two machines, it is essential to have data from the products from both machines. These statements are no more than common sense, but it is not unusual to find decisions being made on misconceived or biased data. In other words, full consideration must be given to the reason for collecting data, the correct sampling techniques, and stratification. There should not be, for example, a disproportionate amount of a certain kind of data simply because it can be collected easily.

Types of Quality Data

Numerical information on quality will arise from:

1. Counting, or
2. Measurement.

Data which arises from counting can only occur at definite points or in 'discrete' jumps. There can only be 0, 1, or 2, etc. defectives in a sample of 10 items. There cannot be 2.86 defectives. The number of imperfections on a polished surface, the number of defects in a length of cloth, the acceptability or unacceptability of the lining of a drum are called ATTRIBUTES. As there is only a two-way classification to consider, attributes give rise to discrete data, which necessarily varies in jumps.

Data which arises from measurements can occur anywhere at all on a continuous scale and is called VARIABLE data. The weight of a tablet, the length of a table, the tensile strength of a piece of rod, are all variables, the measurement of which produces continuous data. If data from variables measurement were truly continuous, they could take any value within a given range without restriction. However, owing to the limitations of measurement, all data vary in small jumps, the size of which are determined by the instruments in use.

The statistical principles involved in the analysis of whole numbers are not usually the same as those involved in continuous measurement. The theoretical background necessary for the analysis of these different types of data will be presented in Chapters 4, 5, 9 and 10.

Recording Data

After data are collected, they are analysed and useful information is extracted through the use of statistical methods. It follows then that data

Date	Percentage impurity					Week total	Week average
	15th	16th	17th	18th	19th		
Time							
8 a.m.	0.26	0.24	0.28	0.30	0.26	1.34	0.27
10 a.m.	0.31	0.33	0.33	0.30	0.31	1.58	0.32
12 noon	0.33	0.33	0.34	0.31	0.31	1.62	0.32
2 p.m.	0.32	0.34	0.36	0.32	0.32	1.66	0.33
4 p.m.	0.28	0.24	0.26	0.28	0.27	1.33	0.27
6 p.m.	0.27	0.25	0.24	0.28	0.26	1.30	0.26
Day total	1.77	1.73	1.81	1.79	1.73		
Day average	0.30	0.29	0.30	0.30	0.29	8.83	0.29
Operator	*A. Ridgeworth*						

Week commencing 15 February

Fig. 2.1   Data collection sheet for impurity in a chemical product

should be obtained in such a form that will simplify the subsequent analysis. The first basic rule is to record the nature of the data. This will avoid the problem of tables of numbers, the origin and relevance of which has been lost or forgotten. It is necessary to record not only the purpose of the measurement and its characteristics, but also the date, any sampling plan and any instruments used, the method, the person collecting the data, and so on.

Data should be recorded in such a way that it is easy to use. Simple calculations to give grand totals, averages, and ranges are often computed and the data can often be recorded to make these easier. For example, if readings of a product impurity in a chemical process are taken six times a day at 8 a.m., 10 a.m., 12 noon, 2 p.m., 4 p.m., and 6 p.m., then the data sheet should show the times vertically and the date horizontally (Fig. 2.1). If this is done, then the daily total, and hence the averages, can be obtained for each column. Average fluctuations throughout the day may be seen by looking at each line. Skilful design of the data sheet will facilitate easier and more meaningful analysis.

2.3   Histograms

Every day in factories throughout the world data is collected in various forms: data on defective items, yields, diameters of pistons, weights of capsules, lengths of pins, temperature of reactors, numbers of absentees, etc., etc. Much of this potential information can lie dormant or not be used to the full, often due to the lack of a visual presentation.

Table 2.1   Diameters of pistons (mm) – raw data

56.1	56.0	55.7	55.4	55.5	55.9	55.7	55.4
55.1	55.8	55.3	55.4	55.5	55.5	55.2	55.8
55.6	55.7	55.1	56.2	55.6	55.7	55.3	55.5
55.0	55.6	55.4	55.9	55.2	56.0	55.7	55.6
55.9	55.8	55.6	55.4	56.1	55.7	55.8	55.3
55.6	56.0	55.8	55.7	55.5	56.0	55.3	55.7
55.9	55.4	55.9	55.5	55.8	55.5	55.6	55.2

Table 2.2   Diameters of pistons ranked in order of size (mm)

55.0	55.1	55.1	55.2	55.2	55.2	55.3	55.3
55.3	55.3	55.4	55.4	55.4	55.4	55.4	55.4
55.5	55.5	55.5	55.5	55.5	55.5	55.5	55.6
55.6	55.6	55.6	55.6	55.6	55.6	55.7	55.7
55.7	55.7	55.7	55.7	55.7	55.7	55.8	55.8
55.8	55.8	55.8	55.8	55.9	55.9	55.9	55.9
55.9	56.0	56.0	56.0	56.0	56.1	56.1	56.2

Consider the measurements of diameters of pistons presented in Table 2.1. It is impossible to visualise this data as a whole. The eye concentrates on individual measurements and, in consequence, a large amount of study will be required to give the general picture represented. The histogram provides an excellent means of visualising a set of data.

Tally Sheets and Frequency Distributions

Look again at the figures in Table 2.1. Is the average dimension obvious? Can you tell at a glance the high and low dimensions? Can you estimate the range between the highest and lowest values? If the specification is 55.0 $\pm$ 1.0 mm, is the process capable of meeting its specification and is it doing so? Most people cannot answer the questions very quickly but given sufficient time to study the data the questions could be answered.

If the observations were placed in a sequence or ordered from high to low the problems of estimating the average, the high and low readings, and the range (a measure of spread of the data), would be simplified. Some time to study the data would still be required. The ordered observations are given in Table 2.2. After a brief examination, it is apparent that the low value is 55.0 and the high value is 56.2 with a range of 1.2 (i.e. 55.0 to 56.2). The average is probably around 55.6 or 55.7 and the process is not meeting the specification because three observations are larger than 56.0, the upper tolerance.

The tally sheet and frequency distribution are more descriptive ways of presenting the data. To construct a tally sheet, the data may be used either

Table 2.3 Tally sheet and frequency distribution of diameters of pistons (mm)

Diameter	Tally		Frequency
55.0	1		1
55.1	11		2
55.2	111		3
55.3	1111		4
55.4	⊔卌	1	6
55.5	⊔卌	11	7
55.6	⊔卌	11	7
55.7	⊔卌	111	8
55.8	⊔卌	1	6
55.9	⊔卌		5
56.0	1111		4
56.1	11		2
56.2	1		1
		Total	56

in its original form (Table 2.1) or ordered state (Table 2.2). A scale over the range of observed values is selected and a tally mark is placed opposite the corresponding value on the scale for each observation. Every fifth tally mark forms a 'five-bar gate' which makes adding the tallies easier and quicker The totals from such additions form the frequency distribution. A tally sheet and frequency distribution for the data in Table 2.1 are illustrated in Table 2.3.

The Histogram as a Picture

All the methods used so far to present the collected data contain the same amount of information. The tally sheet and frequency distribution provide a more descriptive picture of the 'central tendency' or average, the dispersion or spread, and the range.

The histogram is closely related to the tally sheet. It is usually constructed with the measured values on the horizontal axis and the frequency or number of observations on the vertical axis. Above each observed value is drawn a rectangle with a height representing the frequency on a linear scale. The area of each rectangle is proportional to the frequency of the observation. In our example, one eighth of all the observations have the value 55.6, and one eighth of the total area under the histogram of Fig. 2.2 is contained in the rectangle above that value.

The advantage of the histogram, when compared to raw data, is the ease with which we can see that:

● the lowest value of the thirty observations is 55.0 and the highest value is 56.2.

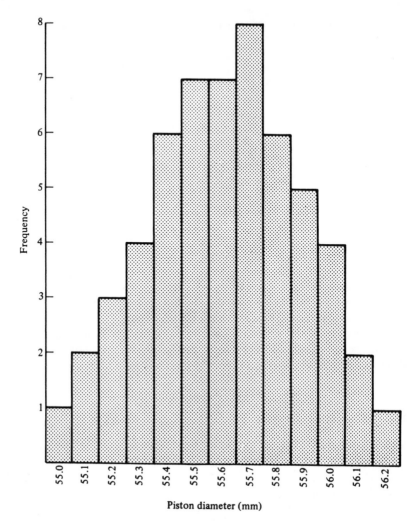

Fig. 2.2   Histogram of data in Table 2.1 – diameters of pistons

● the range is 1.2 (i.e. 55.0 to 56.2),
● the process appears to be centred between 55.6 and 55.7,
● the process is not meeting the specification of 54.0 to 56.0.

It should also be fairly clear that the process is 'capable' of achieving the tolerances since the specification range is 2.0 (i.e. 54.0 to 56.0) and the samples from the process have a range of only 1.2. Perhaps the idea of capability will be more apparent if you imagine the histogram of Fig. 2.2 being moved to the left so that the central values would be nearer to 55.0. If

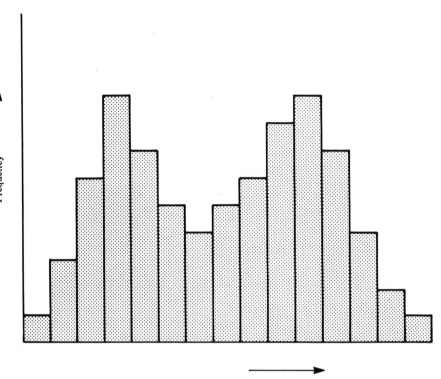

Variable e.g. lengths of wooden pieces from a sawing process

Fig. 2.3   Two peaked histogram – mixed data

a process adjustment could be made to achieve this shift, whilst retaining the same spread of values, all observations would lie within the specification limits with room to spare.

Some other examples of histograms are given in Figs. 2.3 to 2.6. Figure 2.3 is an example of mixed data which could be due to the products of two operators, or two shifts, or two batches being mixed together. Figure 2.4 is the pattern that results when an operator is rounding the results of a measuring operation towards a certain value, or it could be the result of a tendency to record data in even numbers rather than odd numbers. Figure 2.5 shows the result that occurs when a batch of product is sorted but a few 'defectives' still get through, and Fig. 2.6 shows how a histogram may look when the scale of the measuring device is too large.

There may be other explanations for these examples, and there are many other examples possible. The point is that histograms provide the user with a great deal of information, are easily communicated, and inexpensively displayed.

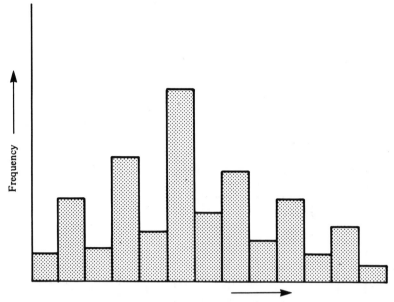

Variable e.g. measures of acidity (pH) from a chemical process

Fig. 2.4   Incomplete histogram

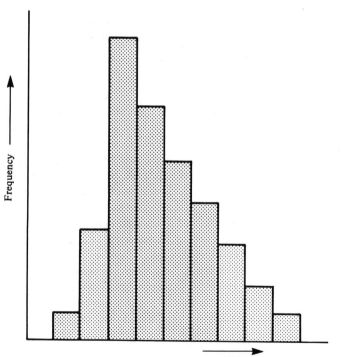

Variable e.g. weights of fertilizer in 20 kg sacks

Fig. 2.5   Truncated histogram

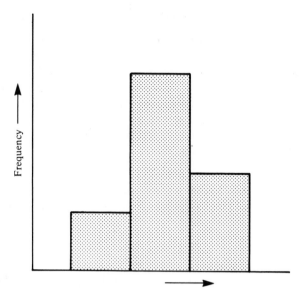

Variable e.g. hardness test results on steel components

Fig. 2.6   Condensed histogram

Table 2.4   Thickness measurements on small pieces of silicon (mm × 0.001)

800	1150	950	950	1050	1000	1050	800
1300	700	1000	750	1000	1250	800	1400
1500	1150	1350	1150	1250	900	1350	1250
1150	700	1250	1050	850	600	1000	1150
1000	1000	1000	1200	1000	750	1100	1300
1100	1050	1050	750	1050	1050	800	1050
1250	1450	900	1000	1200	1200	1150	1300
1150	1450	1350	1250	1100	1050	1150	850
800	900	1550	1250	700	1050	1350	900
1200	1250	1250	1500	1300	750	1200	1200
1000	1050	1100	1100	1000	1350	1050	1200
1000	1250	1000	1400	1150	1150	1300	1100
900	1400	1050	1050	1300	1350	1100	1450
1200	950	700	700	950	1150	1150	800
1350	1500	950	950	1250	500	900	1300
1050	800	850	1350	1300	1500	1550	1000
1100	850	1250	1050	1050	1250	900	1500
1000	1000	900	1450	850	750	1000	1100
1350	1300	1300	950	950	1450	1300	1100
1050	950	1150	1150	950	850	850	1250
750	950	1000	1200	1100	1200	1300	1550
1700	1400	1350	1150	1100	950	1300	1200
1450	1050	1100	1000	1200	1200	1100	1000
1200	1400	1100	1400	950	1150	1450	1100
1100	1650	1500	1200	1600	900	1000	850

Group Frequency Distributions and Histograms

When there are a large number of observations, it is more convenient to present the data in the condensed form of a grouped frequency distribution. The data presented in Table 2.4 are measurements of small pieces of silicon delivered as one batch. Table 2.5 was prepared by selecting cell boundaries to form equal intervals called groups or cells, and placing a tally mark in the appropriate group for each observation.

In the preparation of a grouped frequency distribution and the corresponding histogram, it is advisable to:

1. Make the cell intervals of equal width.
2. Choose the cell boundaries halfway between possible observations.
3. Determine the number of cells from Sturgess Rule which can be used in a simple equation from:

$$K = 1 + 3.3 \log_{10} N$$

where K = number of intervals

N = number of observations

Alternatively, Fig. 2.7 which is based on the above equation offers an even easier way of finding the number of cells to be used.

Table 2.5   Grouped frequency distribution of measurements of silicon pieces

Cell Boundary	Cell Midpoint	Tally				Cell Frequency	Per cent Frequency
475–575	525	1				1	0.5
575–675	625	1				1	0.5
675–775	725	⊞	⊞	1		11	5.5
775–875	825	⊞	⊞	⊞		15	7.5
875–975	925	⊞ 11	⊞	⊞	⊞	22	11.0
975–1075	1025	⊞ ⊞	⊞ ⊞	⊞ ⊞	⊞ ⊞	40	20.0
1075–1175	1125	⊞ ⊞	⊞ ⊞	⊞ 111	⊞	33	16.5
1175–1275	1225	⊞ ⊞	⊞ 1111	⊞	⊞	29	14.5
1275–1375	1325	⊞ 111	⊞	⊞	⊞	23	11.5
1375–1475	1425	⊞	⊞	111		13	6.5
1475–1575	1525	⊞	1111			9	4.5
1575–1675	1625	11				2	1.0
1675–1775	1725	1				1	0.5

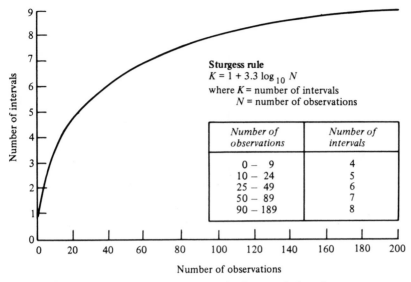

Fig. 2.7   Determination of number of cell intervals for a histogram

The midpoint of a cell is the average of its two boundaries. For example, the midpoint of the cell 475 to 575 is:

$$\frac{575 + 475}{2} = 525$$

The histogram derived from Table 2.5 is shown in Fig. 2.8.

Histograms for Discrete Data

All the examples so far have been of histograms showing continuous data. However, figures for numbers of defective parts, accidents, absentees, defects etc., can be used as data for histogram construction. Figure 2.9 shows the number of badly soldered joints in batches of 1000 printed circuit boards. The distribution is skewed to the right and discrete data will often be found to assume an asymmetrical form.

2.4   Graphs

We have all come across graphs. Television presenters use them to illustrate the economic situation, newspapers use them to show trends in everything from average rainfall to the sales of microcomputers. Unlike the histogram, which has one general shape, a graph can be drawn in many ways. The

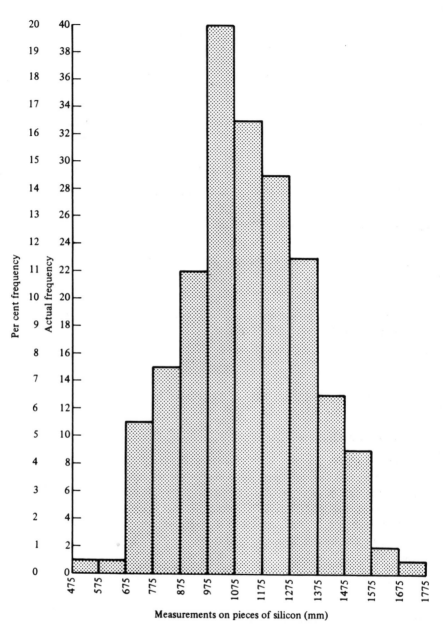

Fig. 2.8   *Histogram of data in Table 4.5 – measurement of silicon pieces*

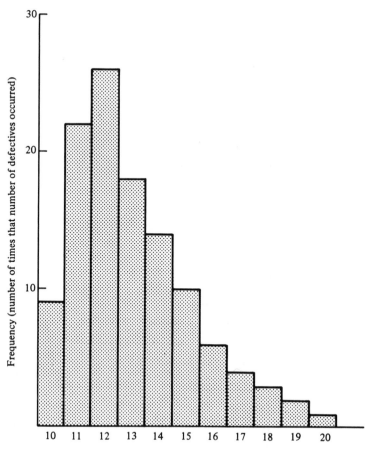

Fig. 2.9   Histogram of attribute data

histogram is one type of graph – a bar graph. Graphs can also be pie charts, line graphs, or pictorical graphs. In all cases, like histograms, they are extremely valuable in quality control and can tell us a lot about a process, batches of product, customer returns, scrap, rework, and many other aspects of a manufacturing operation.

Bar Graphs

We have seen applications of histograms in the preceding section and there will be more of them in the section on Pareto Analysis. Bar charts can be used for other applications, can be drawn horizontally, and

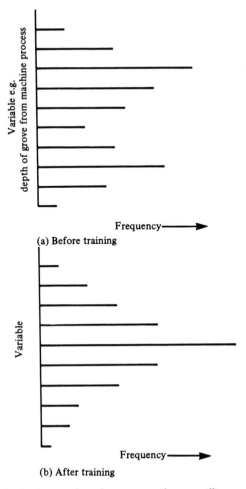

Fig. 2.10   *Line or bar chart–output from a milling machine*

can be lines rather than bars. Figure 2.10 shows a line chart being used to illustrate the difference in a process before and after an operator was trained on the correct procedure to use on a milling machine. In Fig. 2.10a the incorrect method of processing caused a 'bimodal' distribution – one with two peaks. After training, the pattern changed to the single peak or 'unimodal' distribution of Fig. 2.10b. Notice how the graphical presentation makes the difference so evident.

Line Graphs

Line graphs are constructed by drawing a line to represent the data collected from a process or other operation. For example, the difference in

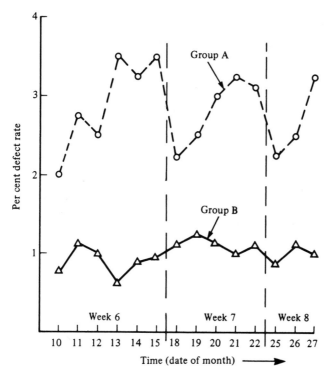

Fig. 2.11 Line graph showing difference in defect rates produced by two groups of operatives

defect rates over a period of time between two groups of workers is shown in Fig. 2.11. A line graph can show changes in a process over time. We can judge the effects of a new machine, various operators or shifts, grade of raw material, or other factors on the process. Fig. 2.12 shows the effect of a new quality control system on overfill in cosmetic packaging.

Line graphs are also useful to detect patterns (Fig. 2.13) and are an essential part of control charts. Sampling risks can also be analysed using curved line graphs where the plotted points are connected by curved lines.

Pictorial Graphs

Often, when presenting results, it is necessary to catch the eye of the reader. A pictorial graph will do this because pictures or symbols of the item under observation are shown. Figure 2.14 shows the number of cars which have been the subject of warranty claims over a twelve month period.

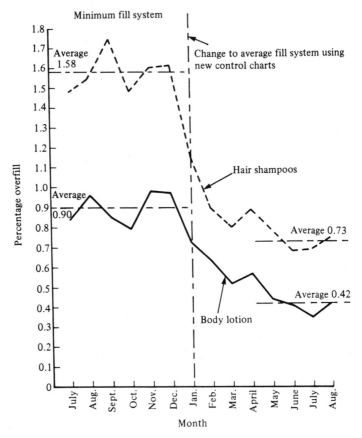

Fig. 2.12   Overfill levels in cosmetic packaging

Pie Charts

Another type of graph is the pie chart which has the advantage that a lot of information can be illustrated in a relatively small area. Figure 2.15 illustrates an application of a pie chart in which the types of defects in furniture are shown. From this it appears that defect D is the largest contributor. Pie charts have applications similar to histograms because they are proportioned in the same way.

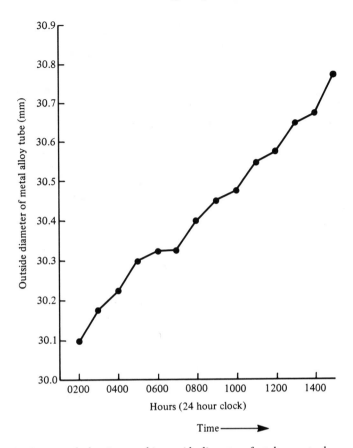

Fig 2.13   Line graph showing trend in outside diameter of a tube as a tool wears over time

The Use of Graphs

All graphs, except the pie chart, are composed of a horizontal axis and a vertical axis and both of these must be kept in mind when drawing or reading a graph. An understanding of what both axes represent and their relationship to each other is essential. The units of measurement and the axes scales are extremely important. Line graphs in particular can be deceiving and the user must be cautious not to mislead the reader through incorrect choice of scales and units.

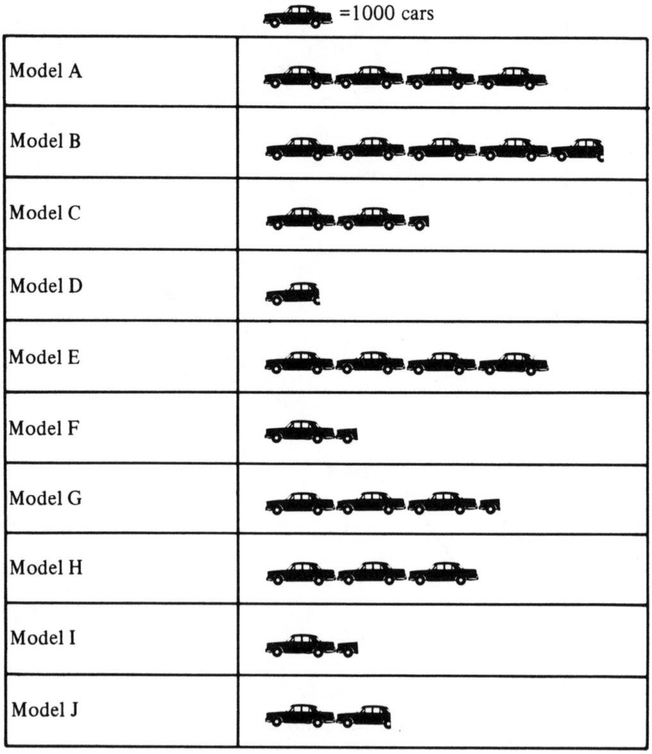

=1000 cars

Model A	
Model B	
Model C	
Model D	
Model E	
Model F	
Model G	
Model H	
Model I	
Model J	

Fig. 2.14   Pictorial graph showing the numbers of each model of car which have been repaired under warranty

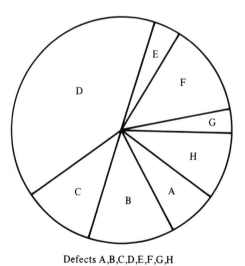

Defects A,B,C,D,E,F,G,H

Fig. 2.15   Pie chart of defects on furniture

CHAPTER 3

Using Quality Data in Problem Solving

3.1 Pareto Analysis

In all things we do in life there is a tendency to find that most of our problems arise from a few of the sources. The Italian economist Vilfredo Pareto used this concept when he approached the distribution of wealth in his country at the turn of the last century. He observed that 80 to 90 per cent of Italy's wealth lay in the hands of 10 to 20 per cent of the population. A similar distribution has been found empirically to be true in many other fields, including quality. For example, 80 per cent of the defects will arise from 20 per cent of the causes; 80 per cent of the complaints originate from 20 per cent of the customers. These observations have become known as part of Pareto's Law or the 80/20 rule.

The technique of arranging data according to priority or importance and tying it to a problem-solving framework is called Pareto Analysis. This is a formal procedure which is readily teachable, easily understood and very effective. Pareto diagrams or charts are used extensively by quality circles all over the world; indeed the technique has become fundamental to their operation for identifying the really important problems and establishing priorities for action.

Pareto Analysis Procedures

There are always many aspects of factory production that require improvement: the number of defectives, process capability, scrap, rework etc., etc. Each problem comprises many smaller problems and it is often difficult to know which ones to tackle to be most effective. For example, Table 3.1 gives some data on the reasons for batches of a dyestuff product being scrapped or reworked. A definite procedure is needed to transfom this data to form a basis for action.

It is quite obvious that two types of Pareto Analysis are possible here to identify the areas which should receive priority attention. One is based on

Table 3.1

SCRIPTAGREEN-A Plant B		Batches Scrapped/Reworked		
		Period 05-07 incl.		
Batch No.	*Reason for Scrap/Rework*	*Labour Cost (£)*	*Material Cost (£)*	*Plant Cost (£)*
05-005	Moisture content high	500	50	100
05-011	Excess insoluble matter	500	nil	125
05-018	Dyestuff contamination	4,000	22,000	14,000
05-022	Excess insoluble matter	500	nil	125
05-029	Low melting point	1,000	500	3,500
05-035	Moisture content high	500	50	100
05-047	Conversion process failure	4,000	22,000	14,000
05-058	Excess insoluble matter	500	nil	125
05-064	Excess insoluble matter	500	nil	125
05-066	Excess insoluble matter	500	nil	125
05-076	Low melting point	1,000	500	3,500
05-081	Moisture content high	500	50	100
05-086	Moisture content high	500	50	100
05-104	High iron content	500	nil	2,000
05-107	Excess insoluble matter	500	nil	125
05-111	Excess insoluble matter	500	nil	125
05-132	Moisture content high	500	50	100
05-140	Low melting point	1,000	500	3,500
05-150	Dyestuff contamination	4,000	22,000	14,000
05-168	Excess insoluble matter	500	nil	125
05-170	Excess insoluble matter	500	nil	125
05-178	Moisture content high	500	50	100
05-179	Excess insoluble matter	500	nil	125
05-179	Excess insoluble matter	500	nil	125
05-189	Low melting point	1,000	500	3,500
05-192	Moisture content high	500	50	100
05-208	Moisture content high	500	50	100
06-001	Conversion process failure	4,000	22,000	14,000
06-003	Excess insoluble matter	500	nil	125
06-015	Phenol content $> 1\%$	1,500	1,300	2,000
06-024	Moisture content high	500	50	100
06-032	Unacceptable application	2,000	4,000	4,000
06-041	Excess insoluble matter	500	nil	125
06-057	Moisture content high	500	50	100
06-061	Excess insoluble matter	500	nil	125
06-064	Low melting point	1,000	500	3,500
06-069	Moisture content high	500	50	100
06-071	Moisture content high	500	50	100
06-078	Excess insoluble matter	500	nil	125
06-082	Excess insoluble matter	500	nil	125
06-094	Low melting point	1,000	500	3,500
06-103	Low melting point	1,000	500	3,500
06-112	Excess insoluble matter	500	nil	125
06-126	Excess insoluble matter	500	nil	125
06-131	Moisture content high	500	50	100

Table 3.1   *(Continued)*

| SCRIPTAGREEN–A
Plant B | | Batches Scrapped/Reworked | | |
| | | Period 05–07 incl. | | |
Batch No.	Reason for Scrap/Rework	Labour Cost (£)	Material Cost (£)	Plant Cost (£)
06–147	Unacceptable absorption spectrum	500	50	400
06–150	Excess insoluble matter	500	nil	125
06–151	Moisture content high	500	50	100
06–161	Excess insoluble matter	500	nil	125
06–165	Moisture content high	500	50	100
06–172	Moisture content high	500	50	100
06–186	Excess insoluble matter	500	nil	125
06–198	Low melting point	1,000	500	3,500
06–202	Dyestuff contamination	4,000	22,000	14,000
06–214	Excess insoluble matter	500	nil	125
07–010	Excess insoluble matter	500	nil	125
07–021	Conversion process failure	4,000	22,000	14,000
07–033	Excess insoluble matter	500	nil	125
07–051	Excess insoluble matter	500	nil	125
07–057	Phenol content $> 1\%$	1,500	1,300	2,000
07–068	Moisture content high	500	50	100
07–072	Dyestuff contamination	4,000	22,000	14,000
07–077	Excess insoluble matter	500	nil	125
07–082	Moisture content high	500	50	100
07–087	Low melting point	1,000	500	3,500
07–097	Moisture content high	500	50	100
07–116	Excess insoluble matter	500	nil	125
07–117	Excess insoluble matter	500	nil	125
07–118	Excess insoluble matter	500	nil	125
07–121	Low melting point	1,000	500	3,500
07–131	High iron content	500	nil	2,000
07–138	Excess insoluble matter	500	nil	125
07–153	Moisture content high	500	50	100
07–159	Low melting point	1,000	500	3,500
07–162	Excess insoluble matter	500	nil	125
07–168	Moisture content high	500	50	100
07–174	Excess insoluble matter	500	nil	125
07–178	Moisture content high	500	50	100
07–185	Unacceptable chromatogram	500	1,750	2,250
07–195	Excess insoluble matter	500	nil	125
07–197	Moisture content high	500	50	100

the frequency of each cause of scrap/rework and the other is based on cost. It is reasonable to assume that both types of analysis will be required. The identification of the most frequently occurring reason should enable the total number of batches scrapped or requiring rework to be reduced. This may be necessary to improve plant operator morale which may be adversely affected by a high proportion of output being rejected. Analysis

Table 3.2   Frequency distribution and total cost of dyestuff batches scrapped/reworked

Reason for Scrap/Rework	Tally	Frequency	Cost per Batch (£)	Total Cost (£)
Moisture content high	ШІ ШІ ШІ ШІ ШІ 111	23	650	14,950
Excess insoluble matter	ШІ ШІ ШІ ШІ ШІ 11	32	625	20,000
Dyestuff contamination	1111	4	40,000	160,000
Low melting point	ШІ ШІ 1	11	5,000	55,000
Conversion Process failure	111	3	40,000	120,000
High iron content	11	2	2,500	5,000
Phenol content > 1%	11	2	4,800	9,600
Unacceptable application	1	1	10,000	10,000
Unacceptable absorption spectrum	1	1	950	950
Unacceptable chromatogram	1	1	4,500	4,500

using cost as the basis will be necessary to derive the greatest financial benefit from the effort exerted. We shall use a generalizable stepwise procedure to perform both of these analyses.

Step 1.   List all the Elements

This list should be exhaustive to preclude the inadvertent drawing of inappropriate conclusions. In this case the reasons may be listed as they occur in Table 3.1. They are: moisture content high, excess insoluble matter, dyestuff contamination, low melting point, conversion process failure, high iron content, phenol content > 1%, unacceptable application, unacceptable absorption spectrum, unacceptable chromatogram.

Step 2. Measure the Elements

It is essential to use the same unit of measure for each element. It may be in cash value, time, frequency, number or amount, depending on the element. In the scrap and rework case, the elements – reasons – may be measured in terms of frequency, labour cost, material cost, plant cost and total cost. We shall use the first and the last – frequency and total cost. The tally chart, frequency distribution and cost calculations are shown in Table 3.2.

Step 3. Rank the Elements

This ordering takes place according to the measures and not the classification. This is the crucial difference between a Pareto distribution and the usual frequency distribution and is particularly important for numerically classified elements. For example, Fig. 3.1 shows the comparison between the frequency and Pareto distributions from the same data on pin lengths. The two distributions are ordered in contrasting fashion with the frequency distribution structured by element value and the Pareto arranged by the measurement values on the element.

To return to the scrap and rework case, Table 3.3 shows the reasons ranked according to frequency of occurrence, whilst Table 3.4 has them in order of decreasing cost.

Step 4. Create Cumulative Distributions

The measures are cumulated from the highest ranked to the lowest, and each cumulative frequency shown as a percentage of the total. The elements are also cumulated and shown as a percentage of the total. Tables 3.3 and 3.4 show these calculations for the scrap and rework data – for frequency of occurrence and total cost respectively. The important thing to remember about the cumulative element distribution is that the gaps between each element should be equal. If they are not, then an error has been made in the calculations or reasoning. The most common mistake is to confuse the frequency of measure with elements.

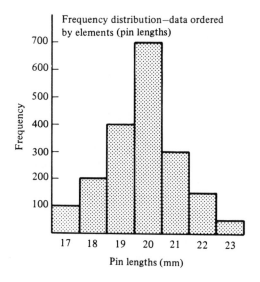

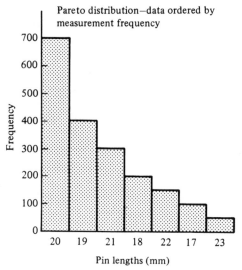

Fig. 3.1   Comparison between frequency and Pareto distribution (pin lengths)

Step 5. Draw the Pareto Curve
The cumulative percentage distributions are plotted on linear graph paper. The cumulative percentage measure is plotted on the vertical axis against the cumulative percentage element along the horizontal axis. Figures 3.2 and 3.3 are the respective Pareto curves for frequency and total cost of reasons for the scrapped/reworked batches of dyestuff product.

Table 3.3   Scrap/Rework – Pareto analysis of frequency of reasons

Reason for Scrap/Rework	Frequency	Cum. Freq.	% of Total
Excess insoluble matter	32	32	40.00
Moisture content high	23	55	68.75
Low melting point	11	66	82.50
Dyestuff contamination	4	70	87.50
Conversion process failure	3	73	91.25
High iron content	2	75	93.75
Phenol content $> 1\%$	2	77	96.25
Unacceptable:			
Absorption spectrum	1	78	97.50
Application	1	79	98.75
Chromatogram	1	80	100.00

Table 3.4   Scrap/Rework – Pareto analysis of total costs

Reasons for Scrap/Rework	Total Cost	Cum. Cost	Cum. % of Grand Total
Dyestuff contamination	160,000	160,000	40.0
Conversion process failure	120,000	280,000	70.0
Low melting point	55,000	335,000	83.75
Excess insoluble matter	20,000	355,000	88.75
Moisture content high	14,950	369,950	92.5
Unacceptable application	10,000	379,950	95.0
Phenol content $> 1\%$	9,600	389,550	97.4
High iron content	5,000	394,550	98.65
Unacceptable chromatogram	4,500	399,050	99.75
Unacceptable abs. spectrum	950	400,000	100.0

Step 6. Interpret the Pareto Curves

The aim of Pareto analysis in problem solving is to highlight the elements which should be examined first. A useful first step is to draw a vertical line from the 20%–30% area of the horizontal axis. This has been done in both Figs. 3.2 and 3.3 and shows that:

1. 30% of the reasons are responsible for 82.5% of all the batches being scrapped or requiring rework. The reasons are:
   excess insoluble matter (40%),
   moisture content high (28.75%), and
   low melting point (13.75%).

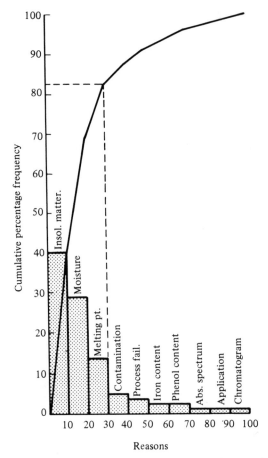

Fig. 3.2   Pareto analysis by frequency – reasons for scrap/rework

2. 30% of the reasons for scrapped or reworked batches cause 83.75% of
   the total cost. The reasons are:
   dyestuff contamination (40%),
   conversion process failure (30%), and
   low melting point (13.75%).

These are often called the 'A' items or the 'vital few' which have been
highlighted for special attention. It is quite clear that if the objective is to
reduce costs, then contamination must be tackled as a priority. Even
though this has occurred only four times in 80 batches, the costs of
scrapping the whole batch are relatively very large. Similarly, concentration
on the problem of excess insoluble matter will have the biggest effect on
reducing the number of batches which require to be reworked.

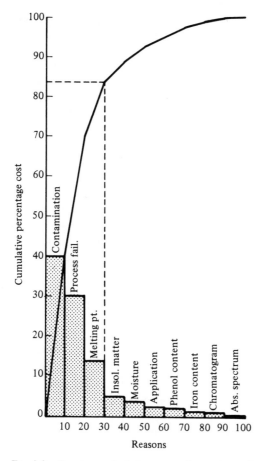

Fig. 3.3 Pareto analysis by costs of scrap/rework

It is conventional to further arbitrarily divide the remaining 70–80% of elements into two classifications – the B elements and the C elements, the so-called 'trivial many'. This may be done by drawing a vertical line from the 50–60% mark on the horizontal axis. In this case only 5% of the costs come from the 50% of the 'C' reasons. This type of classification of elements gives rise to the alternative name for this technique – ABC Analysis.

Procedural Note

ABC or Pareto Analysis is a powerful 'narrowing down' tool but it is based on empirical rules which have no mathematical foundation. It should always be remembered, when using the concept, that it is not rigorous and that elements or reasons for problems need not stand in line until higher ranked ones have been tackled. In the scrap and rework case, for example, if the problem of phenol content $> 1\%$ can be removed by easily replacing a filter costing a few pounds, then let it be done straight away. The aim of the Pareto technique is simply to ensure that the maximum reward is returned for the effort expelled, but it is not a requirement of the systematic approach that 'small', easily solved problems must be made to wait until the larger ones have been resolved.

3.2   Cause and Effect Analysis

In any study of a quality problem, the EFFECT – such as a particular defect or a certain process failure – is usually known. Cause and effect analysis may be used to elicit all possible contributing factors, or CAUSES of the effect. This technique comprises usage of Cause and Effect Diagrams and Brainstorming.

The Cause and Effect Diagram is often mentioned in passing as, 'one of the techniques used by quality circles'. Whilst this statement is true, it is also needlessly limiting in its scope of the application of this most useful and versatile tool. The Cause and Effect Diagram, also known as the Ishikawa Diagram (after its inventor), or the Fishbone Diagram (after its appearance), shows the effect at the head of a central 'spine' with the causes at the ends of the 'ribs' which branch from it. The basic form is shown in Fig. 3.4. The principal factors or causes are listed first and then reduced to their sub-causes, and sub-sub-causes if necessary. This process is continued until all the conceivable causes have been included.

The factors are then critically analysed in light of their probable contribution to the effect. The factors selected as most likely causes of the effect are then subjected to experimentation to determine the validity of their selection. This analytical process is repeated until the true causes are identified.

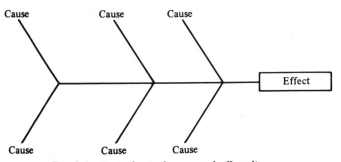

Fig. 3.4   Basic form of cause and effect diagram

Constructing the Cause and Effect Diagram

An essential feature of the Cause and Effect Technique is *Brainstorming*, which is used to bring ideas on causes out into the open. A group of people freely exchanging ideas bring originality and enthusiasm to problem solving. Wild ideas are welcomed and safe to offer, as criticism or ridicule is not permitted during a brainstorming session. To obtain the greatest results from the session, all members of the group should participate equally and all ideas offered are recorded for subsequent analysis.

The construction of a Cause and Effect Diagram is best illustrated with an example.

The production manager in a tea-bag manufacturing firm was extremely concerned about the amount of wastage of tea which was taking place. A study group had been set up to investigate the problem but had made little progress, even after several meetings. The lack of progress was attributed to a combination of too much talk, arm-waving and shouting down – typical symptoms of a non-systematic approach. The problem was handed to a newly appointed management trainee who used the following step-wise approach:

Step 1. Identify the Effect
This sounds simple enough but, in fact, is often so poorly done that much time is wasted in the later steps of the process. It is vital that the effect or problem is stated in clear, concise terminology. This will help to avoid the situation where the 'causes' are identified and eliminated, only to find that the 'problem' still exists. In the tea-bag company, the effect was defined as 'Waste – unrecovered tea wasted during the tea-bag manufacture'. Effect statements such as this may be arrived at via a number of routes, but the most common are: concensus obtained through brainstorming, one of the 'vital few' on a Pareto diagram, and sources outside the production department.

Step 2. Establish Goals
The importance of establishing realistic, meaningful goals at the outset of any problem-solving activity cannot be over-emphasised. Problem solving is not a self perpetuating endeavour. Most people need to know that their efforts are achieving some good in order for them to continue to participate. A goal should, therefore, be stated in some terms of measurement related to the problem and this must include a time limit. In the tea-bag firm, the goal was, 'a 50% reduction in waste in nine months'. This requires, of course, a good understanding of the situation prior to setting the goal. It is necessary to establish the baseline in order to know, for example, when a 50% reduction has been achieved. The tea waste was running at 2% of tea usage at the commencement of the project.

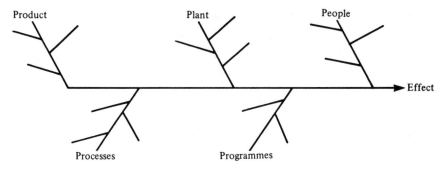

Fig. 3.5   Cause and effect analysis and the 5 'P's

Step 3. Construct the Diagram Framework

The framework on which the causes are to be listed can be very helpful to the creative thinking process. The author has found the use of Lockyer's five 'P's of Production Management very useful in the construction of Cause and Effect Diagrams. The five components of any manufacturing task are the:

Product, including materials and intermediates,
Processes or methods of manufacture,
Programmes or timetables for ordering, manufacture and shipment,
PEOPLE.

These are placed on the main ribs of the diagram with the effect at the end of the spine of the diagram (Fig. 3.5). The grouping of the sub-causes under the five 'P' headings is valuable in subsequent analysis of the diagram.

Step 4. Write the Causes

It is often difficult to know just where to begin listing causes. In a brainstorming session, the group leader may ask each member, in turn, to suggest a cause. It is essential that the leader should allow only 'causes' to be suggested for it is very easy to slip into an analysis of the possible solutions before all the probable causes have been listed. As suggestions are made, they are written onto the appropriate branch of the diagram. Again, no criticism of any cause is allowed at this stage of the activity. All suggestions are welcomed because even those which eventually prove to be 'false' may serve to provide ideas that lead to the 'true' causes. Figure 3.6 shows the completed Cause and Effect Diagram for the waste in tea-bag manufacture.

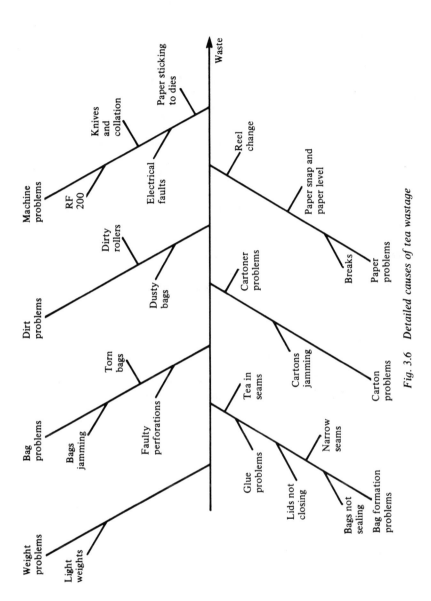

Fig. 3.6 Detailed causes of tea wastage

Step 5. Incubate and Analyse the Diagram

It is usually worthwhile to allow a delay at this stage in the process and to let the diagram remain on display for a few days so that everyone involved in the problem may add suggestions. After all the causes have been listed and the Cause and Effect Diagram has 'incubated' for a short period, the group critically analyses it to find the most likely 'true causes'. It should be noted that after the incubation period the members of the group are less likely to remember who made each suggestion. It is, therefore, much easier to criticize the ideas and not the people who suggested them.

If we return to the tea-bag example, the investigation returned to the various stages of manufacture where data could easily be recorded concerning the frequency of faults under the headings already noted. It was agreed that over a two-week period, each incidence of wastage together with an approximate amount would be recorded. Simple clip-boards were provided for the task. The break-down of fault frequencies and amount of waste produced led to the information in Table 3.5.

From a Pareto analysis of this data, it was immediately obvious that paper problems were by far the most frequent. It may be seen that two of the seven causes (28 per cent) were together responsible for about 74 per cent of the observed faults. A closer examination of the paper faults showed 'reel changes' to be the most frequent cause. After discussion with the supplier and minor machine modifications, the diameter of the reels of paper was doubled and the frequency of reel changes reduced to approximately one quarter of the original. Prior to this investigation, reel changes were not considered to be a problem – it was accepted as inevitable that a reel would come to an end. Tackling the identified causes in order of descending importance resulted in the tea-bag waste being reduced to 0.75% of usage within nine months.

Table 3.5 *Major categories of causes of tea waste*

Category of Cause	Percentage Wastage
Weights incorrect	1.92
Bag problems	1.88
Dirt	5.95
Machine problems	18.00
Bag formation	4.92
Carton problems	11.23
Paper problems	56.10

Application of Cause and Effect Diagrams

The cause and effect diagram is a picture of a brainstorming session. It organizes free-flowing ideas in a logical pattern. With a little practice it can be used very effectively whenever any group seeks to analyse the cause of any effect. The effect may be a quality 'problem' or a desirable effect and the technique is equally useful in the identification of factors leading to good results. All too often desirable occurrences are attributed to chance, when in reality they are the result of some variation or change in the process. Stating the desired quality result as the effect and then seeking its causes in the above way can help identify the changes which have decreased the defect rate, lowered the amount of scrap produced, or caused some other improvement.

3.3 Scatter Diagrams

Scatter diagrams are used to examine the relationship between two factors to see if they are related. If they are, then by controlling the independent factor, the dependent factor will also be controlled. For example, if the temperature of a process and the purity of a chemical product are related, then by controlling temperature, the quality of the product is determined. Figure 3.7 shows that when the process temperature is set at A a lower purity results than when the temperature is set at B. In Fig. 3.8 we can see that tensile strength reaches a maximum for a metal treatment time of B, while a shorter or longer length of treatment will result in lower strength.

In both Figs. 3.7 and 3.8 there appears to be a relationship between the 'independent factor' on the horizontal axis and the 'dependent factor' on the vertical axis. A statistical hypothesis test could be applied to the data to determine the statistical significance of the relationship, which could then be expressed mathematically. This is often unnecessary in the industrial situation where all that is necessary is to establish some sort of association. In some cases it appears that two factors are not related. In Fig. 3.9, the per cent defective polypropylene pipework does not seem to be related to the size of granulated polypropylene used in the process.

Scatter diagrams have application in problem solving following cause and effect analyses. After a sub-cause has been selected for analysis, the diagram may be helpful in explaining why a process acts the way it does and how it may be controlled.

Simple steps may be followed in setting up a scatter diagram:

1. Select the dependent and independent factors. The dependent factor may be a cause on a cause and effect diagram, a specification, a measure of quality, or some other important result or measure. The independent

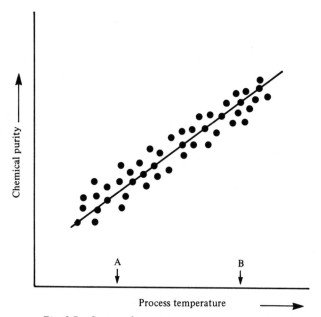

Fig. 3.7   Scatter diagram – temperature v purity

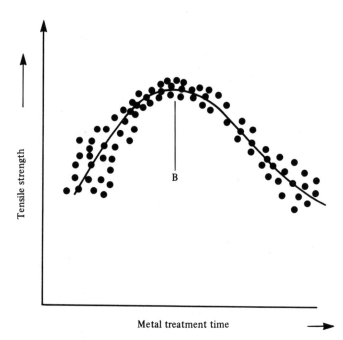

Fig. 3.8   Scatter diagram – metal treatment time v tensile strength

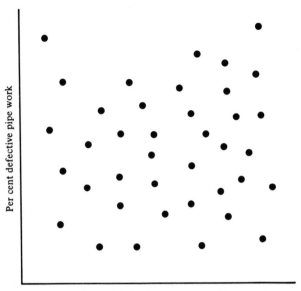

Size of granulated polypropylene used in process

Fig. 3.9   Scatter diagram – no relationship between size of granules of polypropylene used and per cent defective pipe work produced

factor is selected because of its potential relationship to the dependent factor.
2. Set up an appropriate recording sheet for data.
3. Choose the values of the independent factor to be observed during the analysis.
4. For the selected values of the independent factor, collect observations for the dependent factor and record on the data sheet.
5. Plot the points on the scatter diagram, using the horizontal axis for the independent factor and the vertical axis for the dependent factor.
6. Analyse the diagram.

This type of analysis is yet another step in the systematic approach to quality control.

3.4   Statistical Process Control

Statistical process control (SPC) procedures exist because there is variation in the characteristics of manufactured articles. The inherent variability of every manufacturing process causes the products to differ one from another. If this variability is considerable, it is impossible to predict the value of the characteristic of any single item. Using statistical methods, however, it is possible to take meagre knowledge of individual items and turn it into meaningful statements, which may then be used to make decisions about the process or batch of products.

100 Per Cent Inspection or Sampling?

Anyone who has purchased fruit from a market stall will have lifted two or three of the shining red apples from the top of the display to examine the ones beneath. In doing so they will have taken a sample to ensure that the top layer is representative of those below.

In many everyday activities we take samples to estimate the quality of the 'population' from the quality of the 'sample'. This begs the question, 'why not look at the entire population, and then the need for an estimate will be removed?' There are a number of answers to this and one or more may apply in any particular case.

Consider the letters on this page to be a batch of products. Each letter represents one item and each letter 'r' is a defective. Estimate, as quickly as you can, the quality level of this batch of products by carrying out 100 per cent inspection. That is, count every letter 'r' on the page, and time yourself in the process. Now select, at random, one in ten lines of printing and count the number of times the letter 'r' appears on those lines only, again timing yourself. Multiply the total number by 10 and you have an estimate of the quality level by sampling. Compare the results from 100 per cent and sample inspection and the times taken.

In this type of monotonous, repetitive, inspection procedure, 100 per cent inspection generally turns out to be something less than 100 per cent. Monotonous tasks have a way of making people behave in a monotonous manner, which cause them to stop thinking about the job in hand. Research has shown that this causes at least 15 per cent of the defectives present to be missed during 100 per cent inspection and that inspecting a sample gives a higher, more consistent detection rate. Various workers have demonstrated the inadequacy of 100 per cent inspection:

Piston ring defects	33% missed.
Screw defects	32% missed.
Electronic circuit board defects	17% missed.
X-rays for tuberculosis	25% missed.
Dental X-rays for decay	15% missed.

It follows then, that to be fairly sure of catching every defect in electronic circuit boards, for example, 100 per cent inspection must be carried out three times. This should pick up 99.5 per cent of the defects. If extreme precision or human life is involved, an alternative to human 100 per cent inspection must be found, e.g. automatic testing equipment or multiple inspection.

Even if you have a particular aptitude for carrying out repetitive tasks, and have not missed many of the defective letters, the time taken, and hence the cost, for 100 per cent inspection will be far greater than that involved in taking samples. If items can be inspected or tested as quickly as they are produced, then arguments are often found for attempting 100% inspection. In this case, however, the costs of inspection must be examined. Whether the inspection costs are included in the overhead or are a direct cost allocated to specific products is of no consequence; they are manufacturing costs which must be absorbed by the company, but which may be minimized by the use of appropriate sampling schemes.

A situation in which sampling must be preferred to 100 per cent inspection is when conducting the test may destroy the product. The testing of strengths of material, the dissolution of pharmaceutical preparations, the drilling of metal products for analyses samples, and the determination of expected life of electrical light bulbs are just a few examples of where the product is destroyed during inspection. In these and many other cases, a sample must obviously be used to estimate the characteristics of the whole population.

In SPC it is vital that samples are taken randomly. This means very simply that each individual item in the population – the batch of products or the output from the processor – has an equal chance of being chosen. To select always the top pallet from a stack in a warehouse is not random sampling. A common error in process control is to take samples at very regular intervals, with the accompanying danger of failing to observe a cyclical pattern. It is much better, for example, to take samples at 9.05 a.m., 9.29 a.m., 10.02 a.m., 10.17 a.m., and 10.55 a.m., than at exactly 9.00 a.m., 9.30 a.m., 10.00 a.m., and 11.00 a.m.

Statistical Quality Control Techniques

Statistical quality control (SQC) techniques can be used to assess the degree of conformance of raw materials, processes, and products to previously agreed specifications. They can be put to use in short run/small batch production) high volume, or continuous manufacture. In essence, a representative, random sample is selected from the population, which may be a batch of finished products or the output from a process. From an analysis of the sample it is possible to make decisions regarding the whole batch, or the current performance of the process. Furthermore, the risks involved may be specified before any samples are taken. It is important to realize that neither SQC nor 100 per cent inspection can guarantee the quality of the products.

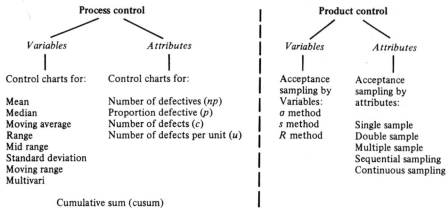

Fig. 3.10   Statistical quality control (SQC) techniques

The techniques of SQC can be classified broadly into two groups as shown in Fig. 3.10. Process control during manufacture is the essence of SQC and should be given priority by those who are hoping actually to control quality, for this can only happen at the point of manufacture. The techniques of statistical process control (SPC) form the basis of the remaining chapters of this book.

At the basis of the theory of process control is a differentiation of the causes of variation in quality during manufacture. Certain variations in the quality of products belong to the category of chance or random variations, about which little may be done, other than to revise the process. This type of variation is the sum of the effects of a complex interaction of 'random' or 'common' causes, each of which is slight. When random variation alone exists, no major part of it may be traced to a single cause. The set of random causes which produces variation in the quality of manufactured product may include: draughts, atmospheric temperature changes, passing traffic or machine vibrations, electrical fluctuations and slight changes in an operator's physical and emotional condition. This is analogous to the set of forces which cause a coin to turn up heads or tails when tossed.

When only random variations are present in a process, the process is considered to be 'in statistical control'. There is also variation in test equipment and test procedures, whether used to measure a physical dimension, an electronic or a chemical characteristic, or any other property. The inherent variation in testing contributes to the overall process variability and is always an important factor.

Causes of variation which are large in magnitude and readily identified are classified as 'assignable' or 'special' causes. For the most part, these consist of relatively large changes in: plant, processes, operators, materials, and other factors. When an assignable cause of variation is present, process variability will be excessive and the manufacturing process is classified as 'out of control' or beyond the expected random variation.

It is important to determine the extent of variability when a process is in control, so that control systems may be set up to detect the presence of assignable causes.

A systematic study of a production process provides knowledge of the variability or capability of the process and the potential sources of defective produce. This information can then be fed back quickly to the product design and production technology functions. Knowledge of the current state of a process enables a more balanced judgement of equipment, both with regard to the tasks within its capability and its rational utilization.

In Chapter 2 a distinction was made between different types of data – VARIABLES and ATTRIBUTES. It was pointed out that they are governed by different statistical laws, which affect the method of controlling the process. In the next five chapters we shall deal with the techniques which are appropriate for the control of variables and Chapters 9 and 10 will present the methods to be applied in attributes control. Many of the underlying concepts are similar, it is really only the statistical theories which differ.

CHAPTER 4

Measurement of Process Variation by Variables

4.1 Accuracy and Precision

In the measurement of process variation by variables, confusion often exists between the accuracy and precision of a process. An analogy may help to clarify the meaning of these terms.

Four archers shoot a number of arrows at four different targets. The results of their efforts are shown in Fig. 4.1. Archer 1 has fired all his arrows into the bull's-eye and may be described as both accurate and precise. He is

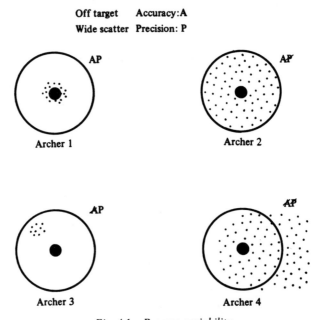

Fig. 4.1   Process variability

Table 4.1 Lengths of 100 steel rods (mm)

144	146	154	146
151	150	134	153
145	139	143	152
154	146	152	148
157	153	155	157
157	150	145	147
149	144	137	155
141	147	149	155
158	150	149	156
145	148	152	154
151	150	154	153
155	145	152	148
152	146	152	142
144	160	150	149
150	146	148	157
147	144	148	149
155	150	153	148
157	148	149	153
153	155	149	151
155	142	150	150
146	156	148	160
152	147	158	154
143	156	151	151
151	152	157	149
154	140	157	151

accurate because on the average his arrows are on target, he is precise because all the arrows are clustered together – there is little spread. Archer 2 is also accurate, since on the average his arrows are on the bull's-eye. He is not, however, as precise as Archer 1 since there is a greater spread of arrows around the target. Conversely, Archer 3 is precise but not accurate. His arrows are tightly grouped together, but on average have missed the bull's-eye. Archer 4 is neither accurate nor precise as he has a wide spread of arrows which are all away from the target.

This analogy is useful when we look at the performance of a manufacturing process producing goods with a variable property. Consider a steel rod cutting process which has as its target a length of 150 mm. The variability of such a process may be determined by measuring a large sample – say 100 rods – from the process (Table 4.1), and shown graphically as a histogram (Fig. 4.2). Another method of illustration is a frequency polygon which is obtained by connecting the mid-points of the tops of each column (Fig. 4.3).

When the number of rods measured is very large and the class intervals small, the polygon approximates to a curve, called the frequency curve (Fig. 4.4). In the majority of cases, the pattern would take the symmetrical

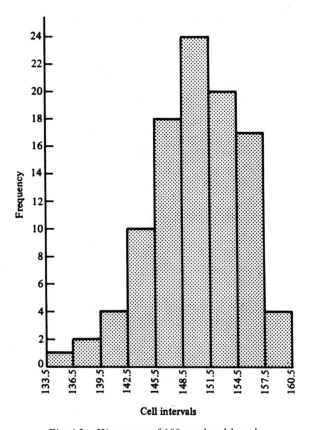

Fig. 4.2   Histogram of 100 steel rod lengths

form shown – the bell-shaped curve known as the NORMAL curve. The greatest number of parts would have the target value, but there would be appreciable numbers either larger or smaller than the target length. Parts with dimensions further from the central value would be progressively smaller in number.

It is possible to imagine four relatively different types of process frequency curve, which correspond to the performances of the four archers in Fig. 4.1. These have been superimposed in Fig. 4.5. Hence, process 1 is accurate and relatively precise, as the average of the lengths of steel rod produced is on target, and all the lengths are reasonably close to the mean.

If only random causes of variation are present, the output from a process forms a distribution that is stable over time and is, therefore, predictable (Fig. 4.6a). Conversely, if assignable causes of variation are present, the process output is not stable over time and is not predictable (Fig. 4.6b). For

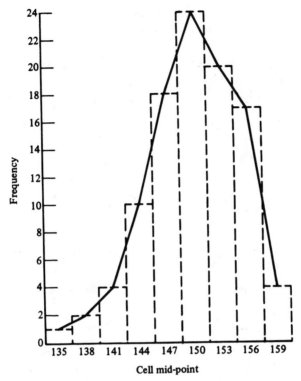

Fig. 4.3   Frequency polygon of 100 steel rod lengths

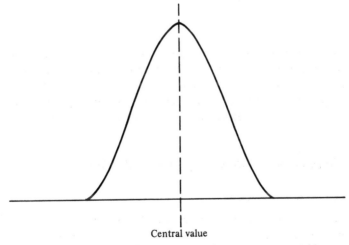

Central value

Fig. 4.4   The normal distribution of a continuous variable

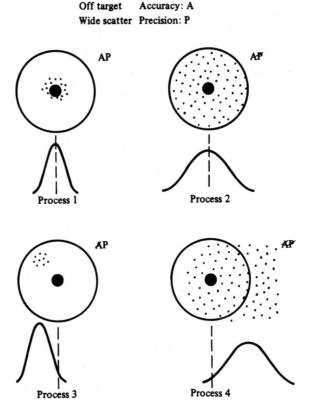

Fig. 4.5   Process variability

a complete interpretation of the data, and before detailed design of a process control system can take place, this intuitive analysis must be replaced by more objective methods of summarizing the histogram or frequency curve. In particular, some measure of the location of the central value must be found together with measures of spread of the data.

4.2   Measures of Location of Central Value

Mean (or Arithmetic Average)

This is very simply the average of the observations, the sum of all the measurements divided by the number of the observations. For example, the mean of the first four measurements of rod lengths in Table 4.1: 144 mm,

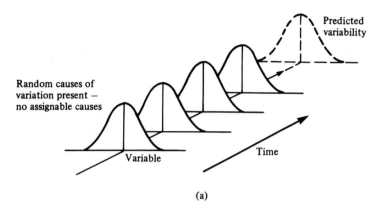

(a)

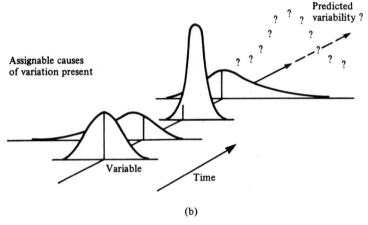

(b)

Fig. 4.6   Random and assignable causes of variation

146 mm, 154 mm, and 146 mm is obtained:

$$
\begin{array}{r}
144\,\text{mm} \\
146\,\text{mm} \\
154\,\text{mm} \\
146\,\text{mm} \\
\hline
\end{array}
$$

Sum   590 mm

$$
\text{Mean} = \frac{590\,\text{mm}}{4} = 147.5\,\text{mm}
$$

When the individual measurements are denoted by x, the mean of the four observations is denoted by $\bar{x}$.

Table 4.2   100 steel rod lengths as 25 samples of size 4

Sample Number	Rod Lengths (mm) (i)	(ii)	(iii)	(iv)	Sample Mean (mm)	Sample Range (mm)
1	144	146	154	146	147.50	10
2	151	150	134	153	147.00	19
3	145	139	143	152	144.75	13
4	154	146	152	148	150.00	8
5	157	153	155	157	155.50	4
6	157	150	145	147	149.75	12
7	149	144	137	155	146.25	18
8	141	147	149	155	148.00	14
9	158	150	149	156	153.25	9
10	145	148	152	154	149.75	9
11	151	150	154	153	152.00	4
12	155	145	152	148	150.00	10
13	152	146	152	142	148.00	10
14	144	160	150	149	150.75	16
15	150	146	148	157	150.25	11
16	147	144	148	149	147.00	5
17	155	150	153	148	151.50	7
18	157	148	149	153	151.75	9
19	153	155	149	151	152.00	6
20	155	142	150	150	149.25	13
21	146	156	148	160	152.50	14
22	152	147	158	154	152.75	11
23	143	156	151	151	150.25	13
24	151	152	157	149	152.25	8
25	154	140	157	151	150.50	17

Hence,

$$\bar{x} = \sum_{i=1}^{n} x_i/n = \frac{x_1 + x_2 + x_3 + \cdots + x_n}{n}$$

where $\sum_{i=1}^{n} x_i/n$ = sum of all the measurements in the sample of size n.

We may regard the 100 results in Table 4.1 as 25 different groups or samples of pieces and calculate, for each group, a sample mean $\bar{x}$. The 25 sample means are shown in Table 4.2.

The mean of a whole population, i.e. the total output from a process, rather than a sample, is given the Greek letter μ. To obtain this true mean of the population, we should need to measure every rod. The Grand Mean $\bar{X}$, the average of all the sample means, however, is a good estimate of the population mean. The formulae for μ and $\bar{X}$ are:

$$\mu = \sum_{i=1}^{N} x_i/N = \frac{x_1 + x_2 + x_3 + \cdots + x_N}{N}$$

where N = the whole population,

$$\text{and} \quad \bar{X} = \sum_{j=1}^{k} \bar{x}_j/k = \frac{\bar{x}_1 + \bar{x}_2 + \bar{x}_3 + \cdots + \bar{x}_k}{k}$$

where k = number of samples taken of size n.

Hence, the value of $\bar{X}$ for the steel rods is:

$$\bar{X} = \frac{147.5 + 147.0 + 144.75 + 150.0 + \cdots + 150.5}{25}$$

$$= 150.1 \text{ mm.}$$

Median

If the measurements are arranged in order of magnitude, the median is simply the value of the middle item. This applies directly if the number in the series is odd. When the number in the series is even, as in our example of the first four rod lengths in Table 4.1, the median is the average of the two middle numbers. Thus, the four measurements in order of magnitude are:

$$144, \ 146, \ 146, \ 154.$$

The median, $(146 + 146)/2 = 146$, is the 'middle item' and has two values equal to or less than it and two values equal to or greater than it. In general, half the values will be not less than that of the median value, and half will be no more than it. An advantage of using the median is the simplicity with which it may be determined.

Mode

A third method of obtaining a measure of central tendency is the most commonly occurring value, or mode. In our example of four, the value 146 occurs twice and is the modal value. It is possible for the mode to be non-existent in a series of numbers or to have more than one value. When data are grouped into a frequency distribution, the mid point of the cell with the highest frequency is the modal value.

Relationship between Mean, Median, and Mode

Some distributions, as we have seen, are symmetrical about their central value. In these cases, the values for the mean, median, and mode are identical. Other distributions have marked asymmetry and are said to be skew. Skew distributions are divided into two types. If the 'tail' of the

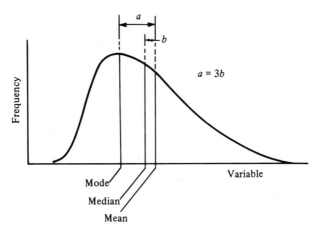

Fig. 4.7   Mode, median and mean in skew distributions

distribution stretches to the right – the higher values, the distribution is said to be positively skewed; conversely in negatively skewed distributions the tail extends towards the left – the smaller values.

Figure 4.7 illustrates the relationship between the mean, median and mode of moderately skew distributions. The approximate relationship is:

Mean – Mode = 3 (Mean – Median)

Thus, knowing two of the parameters enables the third to be calculated.

4.3   Measures of Spread of Values

Range

The range is the difference between the highest and the lowest observations and is the simplest possible measure of scatter. For example, the range of the first four rod lengths is the difference between the longest (154 mm) and the shortest (144 mm), that is 10 mm. The range is usually given the letter R_i. The ranges of the 25 samples of four rods are given in Table 4.2. The Mean Range $\bar{R}$, the average of all the sample means, may also be calculated:

$$\bar{R} = \sum_{i=1}^{k} R_i/k = \frac{270}{25} = 10.8 \text{ mm}$$

where

$$\sum_{i=1}^{k} R_i = \text{sum of all the ranges of the samples.}$$

$$k = \text{number of samples of size } n.$$

The range offers a measure of scatter which can be used widely owing to its simplicity. There are, however, two major problems in its use:

(i) The value of the range depends on the number of observations in the sample. The range increases as the sample size increases. This can be shown by considering again the data on steel rod lengths in Table 4.1:

 The range of the first two observations is 2 mm.
 The range of the first four observations is 10 mm.
 The range of the first six observations is 10 mm.
 The range of the first eight observations is 20 mm.

(ii) Calculation of the range uses only a portion of the data obtained. The range remains the same despite changes in the values lying between the lowest and the highest.

 It would seem desirable to obtain a measure of spread which is free from these two disadvantages.

Standard Deviation

The standard deviation takes all the data into account and is a measure of the 'deviation' of the values from the mean. It is best explained by an example. Consider the deviations of the first four steel rod lengths from the mean:

Value x (mm)	Deviation $(x - \bar{x})$
144	− 3.5 mm
146	− 1.5 mm
154	+ 6.5 mm
146	− 1.5 mm
Mean $(\bar{x}) = 147.5$ m	Total $= 0$

Measurements above the mean have a positive deviation and measurements below the mean have a negative deviation. Hence, the total deviation may be calculated to be zero, which is obviously a useless measure of spread. If, however, each deviation is multiplied by itself, it is said to be squared and, since a negative number multiplied by a negative number is positive, the squared deviations will always be positive:

Value x	Deviation $(x - \bar{x})$	$(x - \bar{x})^2$
144	− 3.5	12.25
146	− 1.5	2.25
154	+ 6.5	42.25
146	− 1.5	2.25
Mean $(x) = 147.5$		Total $= 59.0$

The average of the squared deviations may now be calculated and this value is known as the VARIANCE of the sample. In the above example, the variance or mean squared variation is:

$$\frac{59.0}{4} = 14.75$$

$$= \frac{\Sigma(x - \bar{x})^2}{n}$$

The STANDARD DEVIATION, denoted by the Greek letter sigma (σ), is the square root of the variance:

$$\sigma = \sqrt{14.75} = 3.84$$

Generally $\qquad \sigma = \sqrt{\sigma^2} \quad = \sqrt{\dfrac{\Sigma(x - \bar{x})^2}{n}}$

As with the mean, to obtain the true standard deviation of the population we should need to measure every single item. If a sample is being used to estimate the spread of the process, then the sample standard deviation will tend to underestimate the standard deviation of the whole process. This bias is particularly marked in small samples. To correct for the bias, the sum of the squared deviations must be divided by the sample size less one. In the above example, the ESTIMATED PROCESS STANDARD DEVIATION,

$$s = \sqrt{\frac{59.0}{3}} = \sqrt{19.67} = 4.43$$

The general formula is:

$$s = \sqrt{\frac{\sum\limits_{i=1}^{n}(x_i - \bar{x})^2}{(n-1)}}$$

Using this formula the standard deviation is laborious to calculate. In recent times, however, the computational powers of hand-held calculators has increased to the extent that one which is capable of statistical calculations may be purchased for a moderate price. A much greater problem is that standard deviation is not easily understood.

The meaning of the standard deviation is perhaps most easily explained in terms of the NORMAL distribution. If a continuous variable is monitored, such as the lengths of rod from the cutting process, the volume of paint in tins from a filling process, or the weights of tablets from a pelletising process, that variable will usually be distributed normally about a mean μ. The spread of values may be measured in terms of the population standard deviation, σ, which defines the width of the bell-shaped curve. This is shown in Fig. 4.8 which also shows the proportion of the output

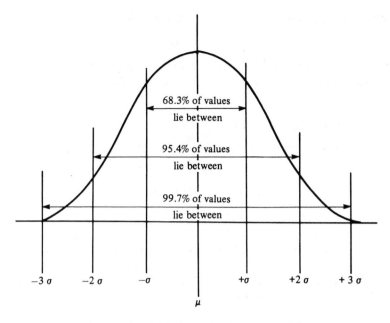

Alternatively: 2.5% of the values lie above $\mu + 1.96\,\sigma$
2.5% of the values lie below $\mu - 1.96\,\sigma$

Similarly: 0.2% of the values lie outside $\mu \pm 3.09\,\sigma$

Fig. 4.8 *Normal distribution*

expected to be found between the values of $\mu \pm \sigma$, $\mu \pm 2\sigma$ and $\mu \pm 3\sigma$.

Suppose the process mean of the steel rod cutting process is 150 mm and that the standard deviation is 5 mm, then from a knowledge of the shape of the curve and the properties of the normal distribution, the following facts would emerge:

- 68.3 per cent of the steel rods produced will lie within ± 5 mm of the mean, i.e. $\mu \pm \sigma$.
- 95.4 per cent of the sheets will be within ± 10 mm $(\mu \pm 2\sigma)$
- 99.7 per cent of the sheets will lie within ± 15 mm $(\mu \pm 3\sigma)$

We can be confident then that almost all the steel rods produced will have lengths between 135 mm and 165 mm. The distance between the two extremes of the distribution, therefore, is 30 mm, which is equivalent to 6σ.

The mathematical equation and further theories behind the normal curve are given in Appendix A. The table on pages 226–7 give the probability that any item chosen at random from a normal distribution will fall outside a given number of standard deviations from the mean. It can be seen, for example, that exactly 95% of the population will lie between:

$$\mu \pm 1.96\sigma$$

In the case of the steel rods with mean length 150 mm and standard deviation 5 mm, 95% of the rods will have lengths between:

$$150 \pm (1.96 \times 5)\,\text{mm}$$

i.e. between 140.2 mm and 159.8 mm.

Similarly, exactly 99.8% of the rod lengths will be inside the range:

$$\mu \pm 3.09\sigma$$
$$\text{i.e. } 150 \pm (3.09 \times 5)\,\text{mm}$$
$$\text{or } 134.55\,\text{mm to } 165.45\,\text{mm}.$$

Hence, on average only 0.1%, or one in 1000 rods will be longer than 165.45 mm, and one in 1000 will be shorter than 134.55 mm.

A special type of graph paper, normal probability paper, which is also described in Appendix A, can be of great assistance to the specialist in handling normally distributed data.

4.4 Sampling and Averages

To understand the logic behind control charts for variables, it is necessary to give some thought to the behaviour of sampling and of averages. If the length of a single steel rod is measured, it is clear that occasionally a length will be found which is towards one end of the tail of the process normal distribution. This occurrence, if taken on its own, may lead to the wrong conclusion that the cutting process requires adjustment. If on the other hand, a sample of four is taken, it is extremely unlikely that all four lengths will lie towards one extreme end of the distribution. If, therefore, we take the average or mean length of four rods, we shall have a much more reliable indicator of the state of the process. Sample means will vary with each sample taken, but the variation will not be as great as that for single pieces. Comparison of the two frequency diagrams of Fig. 4.9 shows that the scatter of the sample averages is much less than the scatter of the individual rod lengths.

In the distribution of mean lengths from samples of four steel rods, the standard deviation of the means, called the Standard Error of the Means, is half the standard deviation of the individual rod lengths taken from the process. In general terms:

$$\text{Standard Error of Means,} \quad \sigma_{\bar{x}} = \sigma/\sqrt{n}$$

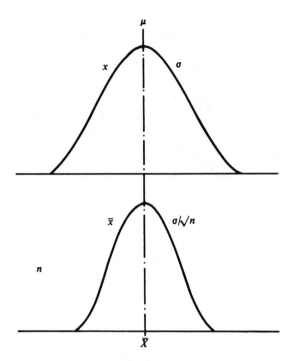

Standard error of means $= \sigma/\sqrt{n}$

Fig. 4.9   What happens when we take samples of size n *and plot the means?*

and when $n = 4$, $\sigma_{\bar{x}} = \sigma/2$, i.e. half the spread of the parent distribution of individual items. In every way $\sigma_{\bar{x}}$ is the same as a standard deviation and normal tables may be used to evaluate probabilities related to the distribution of sample averages. We call it by a different name simply to avoid confusion with the population standard deviation.

The smaller spread of the distribution of sample averages provides the basis for a useful means of detecting changes in processes. Any change in the process mean, unless it is extremely large, will be difficult to detect from individual results alone. The reason can be seen in Fig. 4.10(a), which shows the parent distributions for two periods in a paint filling process between which the average has risen from 1000 ml to 1012 ml. The shaded portion is common to both process distributions and, if a tin volume occurs in the shaded portion, say at 1010 ml, it could either be a volume above the average from the distribution centred at 1000 ml, or one slightly below the average from the distribution centred at 1012 ml. A large number of individual readings would, therefore, be necessary before such a change was confirmed.

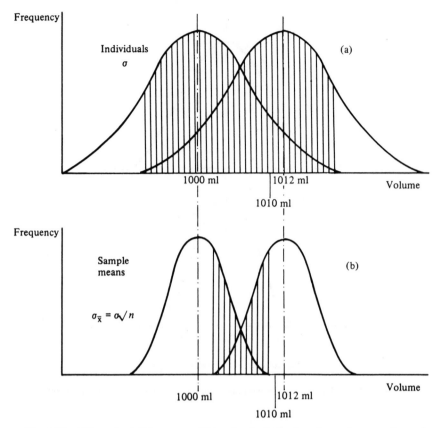

Fig. 4.10   Effect of a shift in average fill level on individuals and sample means. Spread of sample means is much less than spread of individuals

The distribution of sample averages reveals the change much more quickly, the overlap of the distributions for such a change being much smaller (Fig. 4.10(b)). A sample mean of 1010 ml would almost certainly come from the distribution centred at 1012 ml. Therefore, on a chart for sample means, plotted against time, the change in level would be revealed almost immediately. For this reason sample means rather than individual values should be used to control processes.

The Central Limit Theorem

What happens when the measurements of the individual items are not distributed normally? A very important piece of theory in statistical process control is the CENTRAL LIMIT THEOREM. This states that if we draw

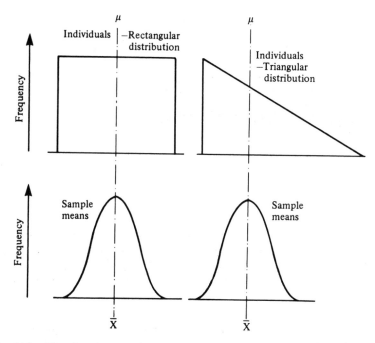

Fig. 4.11 The distribution of sample means from rectangular and triangular universes

samples of size n from a population with a mean μ and a standard deviation σ, then as n increases in size the distribution of sample means approaches a normal distribution with a mean μ and a standard error of the means of: $\sigma/\sqrt{n}$. This tells us that, even if the individual values are not normally distributed, the distribution of the means will tend to have a normal distribution, and the larger the sample size the greater this tendency will be. It also tells us that the Grand Mean of means, $\bar{X}$ will be a very good estimate of the true mean of the population, μ.

Even if n is as small as 4 and the population is far from normal, the distribution of sample means will be very close to normal. This may be illustrated by drawing the distributions of averages of 1,000 samples of size four from each of two boxes of strips of paper, one box containing a rectangular distribution of lengths, and the other a triangular distribution (Fig. 4.11). The mathematical proof of the Central Limit Theorem is beyond the scope of this book and it must be left to the reader to perform the appropriate experimental work if he/she requires further evidence.

CHAPTER 5

The Control of Processes Using Variables Data

5.1 Introduction

To control a process using variable data, it is necessary to keep a check on the current state of the accuracy (central tendency) and precision (spread) of the distribution. This may be achieved with the aid of control charts.

A control chart is a form of traffic signal, the operation of which is based on evidence from samples taken at random intervals during a process. A green light is given when the process should be allowed to run. All too often in manufacturing, processes are adjusted on the basis of a single measurement, a practice which can make a process much more variable than it already is. The equivalent of an amber light appears when trouble is possibly imminent. The red light shows that there is practically no doubt that the process has wandered and that it must be stopped and corrected to prevent production of defective material.

Clearly, such a scheme can be introduced only when the process is 'in control', i.e. is not changing its characteristics of average and spread. Since the samples taken are usually small, typically less than ten, there are risks of errors, but these are small, calculated risks and are based on the various frequency distributions.

There are different types of control charts for variables and attribute data. The most frequently used charts for variables are Mean and Range Charts which are used together. There are, however, other control charts for special applications to variables data. These are dealt with in Chapters 6 and 7. Control charts for attributes data are to be found in Chapters 9 and 10.

5.2 Mean and Range Charts

Mean Charts

The operation of a control chart for sample mean is as follows. Periodically, samples of a given sample size (e.g. four steel rods, five tins of paint, eight tablets) are taken at reasonable intervals from the process when it is

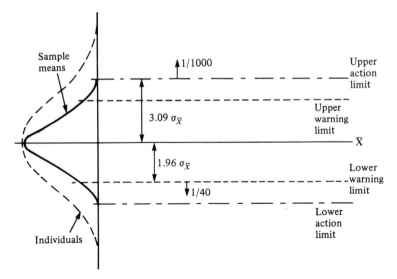

Fig. 5.1   Principles of the mean control chart

believed to be under control and adjustments are not being made. The variable (length, volume, weight, etc.) is measured for each item of the sample and the sample mean recorded on a chart.

Figure 5.1 shows the principle of the mean control chart. If the process is running satisfactorily, we expect from our knowledge of the normal distribution that 99.8% (that is almost all) of the means of successive samples will lie between the lines marked Upper Action and Lower Action. These are set at a distance equal to $3 \cdot 09\,\sigma_{\bar{x}}$ either side of the mean. The chance of a point falling outside either of these lines is less than 1 in 1000, unless the process has altered. If a point does fall outside, the process should be stopped immediately for resetting. This does not normally suggest a serious fault, e.g. it can be due to tool wear, and resetting is all that is necessary. The chances of being right in the decision to stop the process are 999 in 1000.

Figure 5.1 also shows warning limits which have been set $1 \cdot 96\,\sigma_{\bar{x}}$ away from the process mean. The chance of a sample mean plotting outside either of these limits is 1 in 40, i.e. it is expected to happen once in every 40 samples. When it does happen, however, there are grounds for suspicion and the usual procedure is to take another sample immediately, before making a definite decision about the state of the process. Two successive sample means outside a warning line will occur only 1 in 1600 samples (1/40 × 1/40), and occurrence of such points on a mean chart indicates that action to adjust the process should be taken immediately.

It is possible to simplify the calculation of the control limits for the mean chart. In statistical process control for variables, the sample size is usually less than twelve, and it becomes possible to use the alternative measure of spread of the process – the mean range of samples, $\bar{R}$. Use may then be made of Hartley's conversion constant (dn) for estimating the process standard deviation. The individual range of each sample, R is calculated and the average range ($\bar{R}$) obtained from the individual sample ranges:

$$\bar{R} = \sum_{i=1}^{n} \frac{R_i}{k} \qquad \text{where } k = \text{the number of samples of size } n.$$

Then,

$$\sigma = \frac{\bar{R}}{d_n} \qquad \text{where } d_n = \text{Hartley's constant}$$

Now, turning to our previous formulae for the Action and Warning Lines for the mean chart:

Action Lines at $\quad \bar{X} \pm 3.09\,\sigma_{\bar{x}}$

Warning Lines at $\quad \bar{X} \pm 1.96\,\sigma_{\bar{x}}$

We know that $\sigma_{\bar{x}} = \sigma/\sqrt{n}$

Therefore, the limits become:

Action Lines at $\quad \bar{X} \pm 3.09\,\sigma/\sqrt{n}$

Warning Lines at $\quad \bar{X} \pm 1.96\,\sigma/\sqrt{n}$

Substituting $\sigma = \bar{R}/d_n$, the limits become:

Action Lines at $\quad \bar{X} \pm \left(\dfrac{3.09}{d_n\sqrt{n}}\right) \bar{R}$

Warning Lines at $\quad \bar{X} \pm \left(\dfrac{1.96}{d_n\sqrt{n}}\right) \bar{R}$

As 3.09, 1.96, dn and n are all constants for the same sample size, it is possible to replace the numbers and symbols within the dotted rings with just one constant.

Hence,

$$\frac{3.09}{d_n\sqrt{n}} = A'_{.001}$$

and

$$\frac{1.96}{d_n\sqrt{n}} = A'_{.025}$$

The control limits now become:

Action Lines at $\qquad \bar{X} \quad \pm \quad A'_{.001}\ \bar{R}$

Grand Mean   A constant   Mean of

of sample means   sample ranges

Warning Lines at $\bar{X} \pm A'_{.025}\bar{R}$

The constants d_n, $A'_{.001}$, and $A'_{.025}$ for sample sizes $n = 2$ to $n = 12$ have been calculated and appear in Appendix B on page 232.

Using the data on lengths of steel rods in Table 4.2, we may now calculate the action and warning limits for the mean chart:

$$\text{Grand Mean, } \bar{X} = \frac{147.5 + 147.0 + 144.75 + \cdots + 150.5}{25}$$

$$= 150.1 \text{ mm.}$$

$$\text{Mean Range, } \bar{R} = \frac{10 + 19 + 13 + 8 + \cdots + 17}{25}$$

$$= 10.8 \text{ mm.}$$

From Appendix B, for a sample size, $n = 4$, $dn = 2.059$

Therefore, $$A'_{.001} = \frac{3.09}{2.059\sqrt{4}} = 0.75$$

and $$A'_{.025} = \frac{1.96}{2.059\sqrt{4}} = 0.476$$

Alternatively the values of 0.75 and 0.476 may be derived directly from Appendix B.

Now,

ACTION LINES at $\bar{X} \pm A'_{.001}\bar{R}$

Therefore, Upper Action Line $= 150.1 + (0.75 \times 10.8)\text{mm}$

$$= 158.2 \text{ mm.}$$

and Lower Action Line $= 150.1 - (0.75 \times 10.88)\text{mm}$

$$= 142 \text{ mm.}$$

Similarly,

WARNING LINES at $\bar{X} \pm A'_{.025}\bar{R}$

Therefore, Upper Warning Line $= 150.1 + (0.476 \times 10.8) \text{ mm}$

$$= 155.2 \text{ mm}$$

and Lower Warning Line $= 150.1 - (0.476 \times 10.8)\text{mm}$

$$= 145 \text{ mm.}$$

Range Charts

A process is only in control when both the average and spread of the process are in control. A separate chart to control the spread is required. The

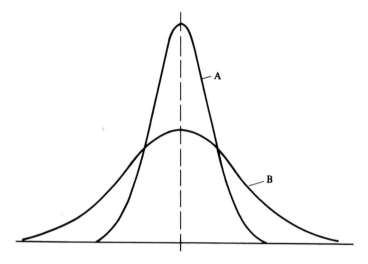

Fig. 5.2   Increase in spread of a process

standard deviation, of a process is one measure of variation. As the sample, n in SPC is usually less than or equal to 12, a more convenient measure of spread is the sample range – the difference between the largest and smallest values. The range chart is very similar to the mean chart, the range of the sample being plotted and compared to predetermined limits. The development of a more serious fault than tool wear can lead to the situation illustrated in Fig. 5.2, where the process collapses from form A to form B, e.g. due to failure of a tool. The ranges of the samples from B will have higher values than ranges in samples taken from A. A range chart is plotted in conjunction with the mean chart and it carries similar action and warning lines to indicate trouble.

The control limits in the range chart are asymmetrical about the mean range since the distribution of sample ranges is a positively skewed distribution (Fig. 5.3). The table in Appendix C provides four constants $D'_{.001}$, $D'_{.025}$, $D'_{.975}$ and $D'_{.999}$ which may be used to calculate the control limits for a range chart. Thus:

Upper Action Line at $D'_{.001}\bar{R}$
Upper Warning Line at $D'_{.025}\bar{R}$
Lower Warning Line at $D'_{.975}\bar{R}$
Lower Action Line at $D'_{.0999}\bar{R}$

For our rods of steel, the sample size is four and the constants are:

$$D'_{.001} = 2.57 \qquad D'_{.025} = 1.93$$
$$D'_{.999} = 0.10 \qquad D'_{.975} = 0.29$$

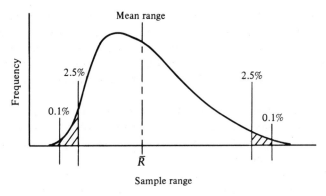

Fig. 5.3   *Distribution of sample range*

As the mean range, $\bar{R}$ is 10.8 mm the control limits for range are:

Action Lines at $2.57 \times 10.8 = 27.8$ mm.
and $0.10 \times 10.8 = 1.1$ mm.
Warning Lines at $1.93 \times 10.8 = 20.8$ mm.
and $0.29 \times 10.8 = 3.1$ mm.

Stepwise Procedure

Although the statistical concepts behind control charts for mean and range may seem complex to the non-mathematically inclined, the steps in setting up the charts are remarkably simple:

1. Select a series of random samples – size n ($n \leqslant 10$).
2. Measure the variable x for each of the sample items.
3. Compute $\bar{x}$ and $\bar{R}$ for each sample.
4. Compute the Grand Mean – $\bar{X}$ and the mean range – $\bar{R}$.
5. Look up the values of:

$$A'_{.001} \quad A'_{025} \quad D'_{.001} \quad D'_{025}$$
$$D'_{.999} \quad D'_{.975}$$

6. Compute action and warning lines for the mean and range charts.

5.3   The State of Control of the Process

Is the Process 'In-Control?'

At the beginning of the section on mean charts it was stated that samples should be taken to set up control charts, when it is believed that the process is under control. Before the control charts are put into use it is important to confirm that, when the samples were taken, the process was indeed 'in statistical control', i.e. the distribution of individual items was reasonably stable. This is done very simply by plotting the results – the sample means and ranges – which were used to set up the control limits, on the charts themselves.

If there has been no movement in the process during sampling, there should be no points outside the action lines on either the mean or range chart. Also there should be no more than about one sample in forty between each warning and action line.

The means and ranges of the 25 samples of four lengths of steel rods, which were used to calculate the control limits for mean and range charts, have been plotted in Fig. 5.4. None of the sample plots lie outside the action lines on either chart. As only one sample mean is plotted between a warning and action line on either side of the mean, the process may be regarded as being in statistical control and the mean and range charts used to control the process.

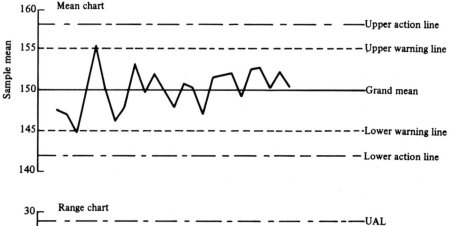

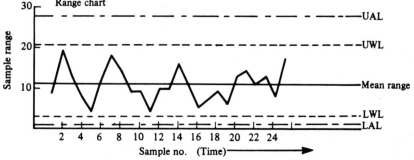

Fig. 5.4   Mean and range chart

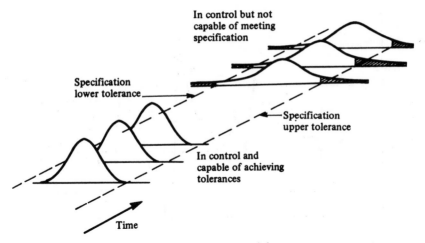

Fig. 5.5   Process capability

Should any sample points plot outside the action lines, or several points appear between the warning and action lines, then the control charts must not be used, and the assignable causes of variation must be investigated. When these non-random causes of variation have been discovered and eliminated, another set of samples from the process is taken and the control chart limits recalculated.

When conducting an initial process study or a reassessment of process capability, approximate control chart limits may be recalculated by simply excluding the out-of-control results for which assignable causes have been found and corrected. The exclusion of samples representing unstable conditions is not just throwing away bad data. By excluding the points affected by known causes, we have a better estimate of variation due to random causes only.

A clear distinction must be made between the tolerance limits set down in the product specification and the limits on the control charts. The former are based on the functional requirements of the products, the latter are based on the actual capabilities of the process. The process may be unable to meet the specification requirements but still be in a state of statistical control (Fig. 5.5). A meaningful comparison of process capability and tolerance can only take place when it has been established that the process is in control statistically.

Controlling the Process

When the process is shown to be in control, then the mean and range charts may be used to make decisions about the state of the process during

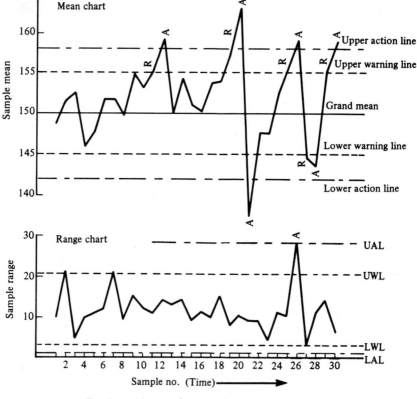

Fig. 5.6   Mean and range chart in process control

manufacture. For example, Fig. 5.6 shows mean and range charts for the next 30 samples taken from the steel rod cutting process. The process is well under control, i.e. within the action lines, until sample 11, when the mean almost reaches the Upper Warning Line. A cautious person may be tempted to take a repeat sample here although, strictly speaking, this is not called for if the technique is applied rigidly. Sample 12 shows that the cautious approach was justified for its mean has plotted above the Upper Action Line and corrective action must be taken. This action brings the process back into control again until sample 19, where the sample mean is in the warning zone – another sample should be taken immediately, rather than wait for the next sampling period. This sample (20) gives a mean well above the action line: corrective action forthwith. But the action results in over-correction and sample mean 21 is below the Lower Action Line. The process continues to drift upwards out of control between samples 21 to 26 and from 28 to 30. The process equipment was investigated as a result of this – a worn adjustment screw was slowly and continually vibrating open, allowing too much rod to pass through the cutting machine.

This situation would not have been identified as quickly in the absence of the process control charts. This simple example illustrates the power of process control charts in both quality control and in early warning of equipment trouble.

It will be noted that 'action' and 'repeat' samples have been marked on the control charts. In addition, any alterations in materials, the process, operators or any other technical changes should be recorded on the charts when they take place. This practice is extremely useful in helping to track down causes of shifts in mean or variability. The chart should not, however, become overcluttered and detailed information is not necessary. Simple marks with cross references to plant notebooks are all that is required.

Trends in the Process

The presence of unusual patterns or trends, even when all sample means and ranges are within the control limits, can be evidence of changes in process average or spread. This may be the first warning of unfavourable conditions which should be corrected even before points occur outside the warning or action lines. Conversely, certain patterns or trends could be favourable and should be studied for possible permanent improvement of the process.

Runs are often signs that a process shift or trend has begun. Appendix D contains tables which are useful in the analysis of sample data for presence of significant runs. A run is defined as a succession of points which are above or below the average. Considering the 25 sample points plotted on the mean chart of Fig. 5.4, they are divided into 13 above the average and 12 below. The sequence starts with a run of 4 points below average, a run of 1 point above average, then a run of length 3 below average, and so on, giving a total of 6 runs above average and 6 runs below – 12 runs in all.

If the process average has been changing gradually during the period of time covered by the 25 measurements then, apart from usual sampling fluctuations, the figures should tend to increase or decrease steadily. In this case, there will tend to be few runs above and below average and the runs will tend to be long. On the other hand, if the figures represent a random sequence of observations from a stable population, then a large number of short runs would be expected.

Reference to Table D1 (Appendix D) for $c = 13$ and $d = 12$ shows that the probability of obtaining 6 or fewer runs with such a split of points is 0.5% – one chance in 200. Thus, with 12 runs there is no reason to suspect that any underlying trends are present.

In cases where the process average has been moving in cycles during the sampling period, it is useful to consider the lengths of runs up and down. A sequence of continually increasing values leads to a run upwards and a run downwards is given by a sequence of continually decreasing values. The 25 samples from Fig. 5.4 will have 24 successive differences between each point on the mean chart. These will be either positive or negative – zero differences being ignored. The sequence of differences begins:

Sample 1.	147.50	
		−ve
Sample 2.	147.00	
		−ve
Sample 3.	144.75	
		+ve
Sample 4.	150.00	
	and so on.	

The complete sequence is: − − + + − − + + − + − − − +
− − + + + − + + − + −

The longest run has a length of 3 upwards. Table D2 (Appendix D) shows that for $k = 25$, the probability of a run up or down of length 7 or more is about 0.1% (one in 1000), whilst a run length of 5 or more will occur with probability of about 5%. Again, there is no evidence of cyclical behaviour in the data.

Five points in a row between $\bar{X}$ and a warning line on one side of the average, or five successive points increasing or decreasing, also indicate a process shift or trend.

5.4   Choice of Sample Size and Frequency of Sampling

In the example used to illustrate the design and use of control charts, 25 samples of four steel rods were measured to set up the charts. Subsequently, further samples of size 4 were taken at regular intervals to control the process. This is a common sample size, but there may be justification for taking other sample sizes. Some guidelines may be helpful:

1. The sample size must be at least 2 to give an estimate of residual variability.
2. As the sample size increases, the control chart limits become closer to the mean. This makes the control chart more sensitive to small variations in the process average.
3. As the sample size increases, the inspection costs per sample increase. One should question whether the greater sensitivity justifies this increase in cost.
4. The sample size should not exceed 12 if the range is to be used to measure

process variability. With larger samples the resulting mean range does not give a good estimate of the standard deviation.

5. When each item has a high value and destructive testing is being used, a small sample size – say 4 or 5 – is desirable and satisfactory for control purposes.
6. A sample size of $n = 5$ is often chosen in industry because of ease of calculation of the sample mean (multiply sum of values by 2 and divide result by 10). However, with inexpensive hand-held calculators, this is no longer necessary.
7. The technology of the manufacturing process may indicate a suitable sample size. For example, in the control of a paint filling process the filling head may be designed to discharge paint through six nozzles into six cans simultaneously. In this case, it is obviously sensible to use a sample size of 6 – one can from each filling nozzle.

It is possible to use a quantitative determination of the sample size. Suppose that we wish to be almost certain of detecting a specified shift in process mean. The specified movement is expressed as a multiple of σ – say $\delta\sigma$. If the process mean moves by $-\delta\sigma$, then the lower action limit will be at a distance from the new process mean of:

$$(3.09\sigma/\sqrt{n}) - \delta\sigma \quad \text{(See Fig 5.7)}$$

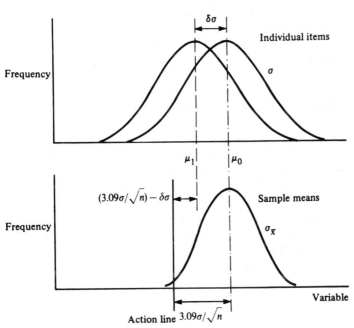

Fig. 5.7   *Determination of sample size*

We should be confident of detecting this movement fairly quickly if 2.5% of the sample means fall outside the action line and 20% (one in five) fall outside the warning line. On this basis, and using the tables describing the normal distribution in Appendix A, the distance of the action limit from the new process mean is:

$$1.96\sigma/\sqrt{n}$$

Therefore,

$$\frac{1.96\sigma}{\sqrt{n}} = \frac{3.09\sigma}{\sqrt{n}} - \delta\sigma$$

$$\delta\sqrt{n} = 3.09 - 1.96$$

and

$$n = (1.13/\delta)^2$$

For example, if we wish to be confident of detecting a change in process mean of 0.5σ i.e. $\delta = 0.5$, then the sample size required is:

$$n = \left(\frac{1.13}{0.5}\right)^2$$

$$= 5, \text{ to the nearest integer.}$$

There are no rules for the frequency of taking samples. It is very much a function of the product being made and the process used. In general, it is recommended that samples are taken quite often at the beginning of the process. When it has been confirmed that the process is in control, the frequency of sampling may be reduced. It is important to ensure that the frequency of sampling is determined in such a way that ensures no bias exists.

5.5   Control Charts for Variables in the USA

Instead of using 3.09 standard errors to calculate upper and lower action lines at 0.001 probability, and 1.96 standard errors to calculate warning lines at 0.025 probability, the Americans use simplified control charts and set an 'Upper Control Limit' (ULC) and a 'Lower Control Limit' (LCL) at 3.0 standard errors either side of the process mean. No warning lines are used. Sample sizes of 5 are commonly used in the USA. To illustrate this method, the following parameters have been obtained by measuring 25 samples of five shaft diameters:

Process Mean, $\bar{X} = 60.50\,\text{mm}$

(this is sometimes given the symbol $\bar{\bar{X}}$ in the USA)

Mean Range, $\bar{R} = 0.101\,\text{mm}$

(in order British standards this is given the symbol $\bar{w}$).

Now, standard deviation of process, $\bar{R} = \bar{w}/d_n$

$$= R/d_2$$

$d_n(d_2$ in USA) $= 2.326$ for $n = 5$, from Appendix B.

Therefore, $\sigma = 0.10/2.326 = 0.043\,\text{mm}$

Standard error of the mean, $\sigma_{\bar{x}} = \sigma/\sqrt{n}$

$$= 0.043/\sqrt{5}$$

$$= 0.019\,\text{mm}$$

Mean Chart

Upper Control Limit (UCL) $= \bar{X} + 3\sigma_{\bar{x}}$

$$= 60.50 + (3 \times 0.019)$$

$$= 60.56\,\text{mm}.$$

Lower Control Limit (LCL) $= \bar{X} - 3\sigma_{\bar{x}}$

$$= 60.50 - (3 \times 0.019)$$

$$= 60.44\,\text{mm}.$$

As with the British system, the calculation of control limits may be simplified to allow use of the mean sample range, $\bar{R}$ directly:

e.g. Upper Control Limit $= \bar{X} + 3\sigma_{\bar{x}}$

$$= \bar{X} + 3\frac{\sigma}{\sqrt{n}}$$

$$= \bar{X} + \frac{3\bar{R}}{d_2\sqrt{n}}$$

$3/d_2\sqrt{n}$ is a constant for a given sample size and this is designated A_2.

Therefore, if $A_2 = \dfrac{3}{d_2\sqrt{n}}$

then the Upper Control Limit $= \bar{X} + A_2\bar{R}$

Similarly the Lower Control Limit $= \bar{X} - A_2\bar{R}$

A_2 may be calculated as above or found from Appendix B for a given sample size.

Hence, for $n = 5$, $A_2 = \dfrac{3}{2.326\sqrt{5}} = 0.58$

$$\text{and the Upper Control Limit (UCL)} = \bar{\bar{X}} + 0.58\bar{R}$$
$$= 60.50 + (0.58 \times 0.10)$$
$$= 60.56\,\text{mm}$$

$$\text{and Lower Control Limit (LCL)} = \bar{\bar{X}} - 0.58\bar{R}$$
$$= 60.50 - (0.58 \times 0.10)$$
$$= 60.44\,\text{mm}.$$

Range Chart

To allow for the use of only one set of control limits, the UCL and LCL on the American range charts are set in between the British action and warning lines. The general formulae are:

Upper Control Limit $= D_4\bar{R}$
Lower Control Limit $= D_2\bar{R}$

Where n is 6 or less, the Lower Control Limit will turn out to be less than 0. Because the range cannot be less than 0, the lower limit is not used. The constants D_2 and D_4 may be found directly from Appendix C for a given sample size, n.

$$\text{For } n = 5,\ D_2 = 0 \text{ and } D_4 = 2.11$$
$$\text{Therefore, the Upper Control Limit} = 2.11 \times 0.10$$
$$= 0.21\,\text{mm}.$$

Additional Rules

American control charts are used in a very similar fashion to those designed with action and warnings lines at 0.001 and 0.025 probabilities respectively. Hence, the presence of one or more points beyond either Upper or Lower Control Limit is evidence of an out-of-control situation, and provides a signal for an immediate investigation of the assignable cause. Because there are no warning limits on the American charts, some additional guidance is usually offered to assist the process control operation. These may be summarized:

1. Approximately two-thirds of the data points should lie within the middle third region of each chart – for mean and for range. If substantially more or less than two-thirds of the points lie close to $\bar{\bar{X}}$ or $\bar{R}$, then the process should be checked for possible changes. It is always worth checking the calculation of control limits before taking elaborate investigative steps.
2. If random causes of variation only are present, the control charts should

not display any evidence of runs or trends in the data. The following are taken to be signs that a process shift or trend has been initiated:

- seven points in a row on one side of the average,
- seven lines between successive points which are continually increasing or decreasing.

It is useful practice for those using the British control chart system, with warning lines, to also apply the two simple checks described above. The existence of the lines at 0.025 probability do, of course, offer a less black and white situation than the UCL/LCL system, so there is less need for the rigorous application of these checks. Whilst it is wise to investigate all signals of possible assignable causes, it must be remembered that they may have been caused by normal variability and that there may be no underlying process problem. If only doubtful evidence of a process problem is found, any action taken will only increase the total variability in the process output. There is clearly little difference between the American and British control charts for mean and range. Far more important than any subtle operating discrepancies is the need to adhere to whichever system has been chosen.

CHAPTER 6

Process Capability for Variables

6.1 Introduction

In manufacturing the usual aim is not to achieve for every steel rod the same length, every piston the same diameter, or every tablet the same weight, but to obtain products within specified limits or tolerances. No adjustment of a process is called for as long as there is no immediate danger of falling outside the tolerance zone. If tolerances have been set for the lengths of steel rods at 150 ± 20 mm., then with a standard deviation, σ of 5 mm., very few will fall outside the tolerances, provided the process has been correctly centred (Fig. 6.1). Conversely, if the spread of the process exceeds the tolerance zone, e.g. 150 ± 10 mm., as in Fig. 6.2, then reject material will inevitably be produced. When this happens, there are three possible courses of action:

(i) Sort out all the products into acceptable – those inside the specified tolerances – and unacceptable. As we have seen in Chapter 3, this is an extremely time consuming and costly activity, as well as being unreliable.

(ii) Reduce the process variability by improving the equipment, the materials, the methods of manufacture, or some other aspect of the

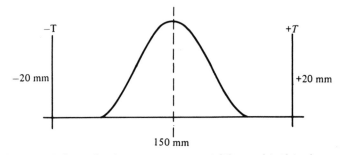

Fig. 6.1   Relationship between process variability and 'wide' tolerances

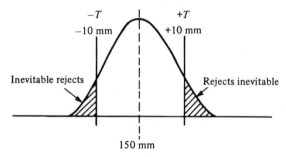

Fig. 6.2 Relationship between process variability and 'narrow' tolerances

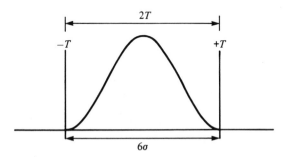

Fig. 6.3 Process capability

process. The training of the operators is frequently found to be an important factor.

(iii) Widen the specified tolerances. This option is always worth consideration, since it may be found that the specification which has been set is unnecessarily tight.

6.2 Relative Precision and Process Capability Indexes

The relationship between process variability and tolerances may be formalized by consideration of the standard deviation, σ of the process. In order to manufacture within the specification, the distance between the upper tolerance ($+ T$) and lower tolerance ($- T$), i.e. $2T$, must be equal to or greater than the width of the base of the process bell, i.e. 6σ. This is shown in Fig. 6.3. The relationship between $2T$ and 6σ gives rise to three levels of precision of the process:

- Low Relative Precision, where the tolerance band is less than or equal to 6σ ($2T \leqslant 6\sigma$),

- Medium Relative Precision, where the tolerance band is greater than 6σ ($2T > 6\sigma$),
- High Relative Precision, where the tolerance band is very much greater than 6σ ($2T \gg 6\sigma$).

These terms may be quantified by the calculation of the Relative Precision Index (RPI). Let us take the minimum width of the tolerance band which is required to avoid making reject material – shown in Fig. 6.3. That is, we must have:

$$2T \geqslant 6\sigma$$

we know that $\sigma = \dfrac{\bar{R}}{d_n} = \dfrac{\text{Mean Sample Range}}{\text{Hartley's Constant}}$

so: $\qquad\qquad 2T \geqslant 6\bar{R}/d_n$

divide each side by $\bar{R}$: $\qquad 2T/\bar{R} \geqslant 6/d_n$

$2T/\bar{R}$ is known as the RELATIVE PRECISION INDEX (RPI) and the value of $6/dn$ is the MINIMUM value of the process RPI to avoid the manufacture of rejects. This minimum may be calculated for each sample size. For example, for a sample size of $n = 4$, dn is 2.059 and the Minimum RPI is:

$$6/2.059 = 2.914$$

The minimum values of RPI for other sample sizes have been calculated and are given in Appendix E, Table E1.

In our steel rod example, the mean range, $\bar{R}$ of 25 samples of size 4 was 10.8 mm. If we are asked then to produce rods within ± 10 mm of the target length, we can see immediately that:

$$\text{RPI} = 2T/\bar{R} = 20/10.8 = 1.852.$$

and, as this value is considerably less than the minimum 2.914, then reject material will be produced – the process is not capable of achieving the design tolerances (Fig. 6.2).

Conversely, if tolerances are widened to ± 20 mm, then:

$$\text{RPI} = 2T/\bar{R} = 40/10.8 = 3.704.$$

and reject material can be avoided if the average and spread of the process and adequately controlled (Fig. 6.1).

The RPI provides a very quick and simple way of quantifying process capability. It is important to stress, however, that the method is only valid for a process which is in statistical control. Using RPI, it is possible to divide processes into the three broad categories already mentioned:

- Low relative precision, when RPI is less than, or very close to the minimum value.
- Medium relative precision, when RPI is just greater than the minimum. In this case, the process can only just meet the specification and strict control must be maintained if no rejects are to be produced.
- High relative precision, when RPI is much greater than the minimum. Here, there is room for the process average to move about without causing rejects and a 'relaxed control' may be allowed (see section 6.4). Table E2, Appendix E indicates the precision of manufacture associated with values of RPI for each sample size.

Any process capability index is a measure relating the actual performance of a process to its specified performance where processes are considered to be a combination of the plant or equipment, the process or method itself, the people, the materials and the environment. The minimum requirement is that three process standard deviations each side of the process mean are contained within the specification limits. This means that 99.7% of output will be within the tolerances. A more stringent requirement is often stipulated to ensure that produce of correct quality is consistently obtained over the long term.

When a process is under statistical control (i.e. only random or common causes of variation are present), a process capability index may be calculated. Process capability indexes are simply a means of indicating the variability of a process relative to the product specification tolerance and we have already seen the use of one – the Relative Precision Index (RPI).

Other indexes, originating in the USA, are Cp and Cpk. To use these indexes, it is first necessary to calculate σ from the average range:

$$\sigma = \bar{R}/d_n \quad \text{or} \quad \bar{R}/d_2$$

Now, $$Cp = 2T/6\sigma$$

and $$Cpk = \text{the minimum of } \frac{USL - \bar{X}}{3\sigma} \quad \text{or} \quad \frac{\bar{X} - LSL}{3\sigma}$$

where USL = Upper Specification Limit

LSL = Lower Specification Limit

Cp indicates the spread of the process (it is obtained from RPI by multiplying by the factor $d_n/6$)

Cpk indicates both the spread and the setting of the process

Values for Cp and Cpk greater than 1 indicate that three process standard deviations either side of the mean are contained within the specification limits or tolerances band. To meet the more stringent requirements of some companies, values of Cp and Cpk must approach

2. Values less than 1 indicate that the process is not capable of achieving the specified tolerances.

A couple of examples should indicate the use of Cp and Cpk.

(i) Process parameters from 20 samples of size $n = 4$ are:

$$\text{mean range } (\bar{R}) = 91 \text{ mgm}, \quad \text{process mean } (\bar{X}) = 2500 \text{ mgm}.$$

Specified requirements are $USL = 2650 \text{ mgm}, \quad LSL = 2350 \text{ mgm}$

$$\sigma = \frac{91}{2.059} = 44.2 \text{ mgm}$$

$$Cp = \frac{2 \times 150}{6 \times 44.2} = 1.13$$

$$Cpk = \text{minimum of} \frac{2650 - 2500}{(3 \times 44.2)} \quad \text{or} \quad \frac{2500 - 2350}{(3 \times 44.2)}$$

$$= 1.13$$

Values of Cp and Cpk are just greater than 1.

(ii) Process parameters:

$$n = 4 \qquad \bar{R} = 91 \text{ mgm}$$
$$\bar{X} = 2650 \text{ mgm}$$

Specified requirements are $USL = 2750 \text{ mgm}, LSL = 2250 \text{ mgm}$.

$$\sigma = \frac{91}{2.059} = 44.2 \text{ mgm}$$

$$Cp = \frac{2 \times 250}{6 \times 44.2} = 1.89$$

$$Cpk = \text{minimum of} \frac{2750 - 2650}{(3 \times 44.2)} \quad \text{or} \quad \frac{2650 - 2250}{(3 \times 44.2)}$$

$$= 0.75$$

The Cp value of 1.89 indicates that the process spread is capable of producing material well within the specified tolerance, but the Cpk value of < 1 suggests that the setting of the process is incorrect.

Any process capability analysis technique, no matter how precise it appears, can give only approximate results. This is true because:

● there is always some sampling variation,
● no process is ever fully in statistical control, and
● no output exactly follows the normal distribution (or any other standard distribution).

Final results should, therefore, always be used and interpreted with caution.

6.3 Proportion Defective Produced and Setting Targets

When it has been shown that a process is not capable of achieving the design tolerances, it may be necessary to determine the proportion of output which will fall outside the specification limits. For example, samples of size 5 are taken from a tablet manufacturing process which is in statistical control. The tablets are weighed and 20 samples have:

$$\text{a grand mean, } \bar{X} = 255 \text{ mgm}$$
$$\text{and mean sample range, } \bar{R} = 11 \text{ mgm}$$

The standard deviation, σ may be calculated:

$$\sigma = \bar{R}/d_n = 11/2.326 = 4.73 \text{ mgm.}$$

If the product specification demands a weight of 250 ± 10 mgm, then how much of the production will lie outside the tolerance zone? The situation is represented in Fig. 6.4. Firstly it is necessary to convert the distance between the process mean and the upper tolerance into units of σ. This is done as follows:

$$Zu = (U - \bar{X})/\sigma$$

where
$U =$ Upper Tolerance

$\bar{X} =$ Grand Mean of Samples (process mean, μ)

$\sigma =$ Process Standard Deviation (estimated from $\bar{R}$)

$Zu =$ Number of standard deviations between U and $\bar{X}$

(termed the standardized normal variate)

Hence, $\quad Zu = (260 - 255)/4.73 = 1.057$

Using the table of Proportions Under the Normal Curve in Appendix A, it is possible to determine that the proportion of tablets lying outside the

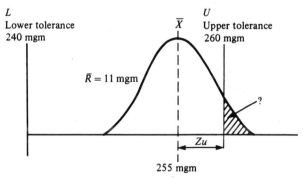

Fig. 6.4   Determination of proportion defective produced

upper tolerance limit is 0.145 or 14.5 per cent. These are two causes of this high level of rejects:

(i) the setting of the process, which should be centred at 250 mgm, not 255 mgm.
(ii) the spread of the process.

If the process were centred at 250 mgm with the same spread it is possible to calculate, using the above method, the proportion of the tablet production which will lie outside the tolerance band:

$$Zu = (U - \bar{X})/\sigma = (260 - 250)/4.73 = 2.11$$
$$Zl = (\bar{X} - L)/\sigma = (250 - 240)/4.73 = 2.11$$

where

$L =$ Lower Tolerance

$Zl =$ Number of standard deviations between $\bar{X}$ and L

Using the values of Zu, Zl, and Appendix A, the proportion of tablets outside each tolerance limit is found to be 0.0175. Therefore, a total of 3.5 per cent of the production will be outside specification, even if the process is adjusted to the correct target weight.

The normal distribution may also be used to determine the target value for a variable to achieve a certain tolerance. For example, a manufacturer is filling one-litre cans with paint and we assume the amounts of paint in the cans vary according to the normal distribution with a standard deviation of 2 ml. If the stated minimum quantity in one can is 1000 ml,

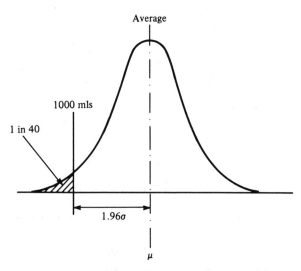

Fig. 6.5   Setting target fill quantity in paint process

what must the average quantity put in a can be if the risk for underfilling is about one chance in forty?

The 1 in 40 (i.e. 0.025 probability) line must be set at 1000 ml. It must also be 1.96σ below the average quantity. This fact is determined from the normal distribution (Appendix A). The average quantity, μ must, therefore, be set at:

$$\mu = (1000 + 1.96\sigma)\,\text{ml.}$$
$$= 1000 + (1.96 \times 2)\,\text{ml.}$$
$$= 1004\,\text{ml.}$$

This is shown in Fig. 6.5.

6.4 Modified or Relaxed Control Charts

In some cases, the inherent variability of the manufacturing process is small compared with the width of the specification tolerance zone. In these cases, the process mean may shift from the central target value without reject material being made. This type of process, which is represented in Fig. 6.6, has High Relative Precision. A different type of chart, called a

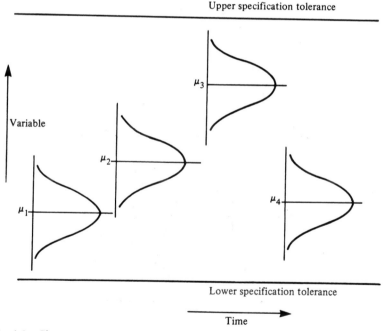

Fig. 6.6   Changes in process average when specification tolerance zone is much larger than process variability

RELAXED OR MODIFIED CONTROL CHART, may be used for this precision class. Such a chart will allow the process mean to wander away from the target value, until it approaches the tolerance limits. How close to the tolerance one allows such a process to move is a matter of some judgement and statistical calculation. If we assume that we will accept 0.1 per cent (1 in 1000) of the output to fall outside each tolerance, then we must maintain the process mean to within a distance of 3.09σ inside each tolerance limit (Fig. 6.7). To set the Upper Action Line (UAL) on a relaxed mean control chart, at $3.09\sigma/\sqrt{n}$ above the highest allowed process mean, requires that the distance between the UAL and the Upper Tolerance, U is known. In Fig. 6.7, this distance is $A''_{.001}\,\bar{R}$, where:

$$A''_{.001}\,\bar{R} = 3.09\sigma - 3.09\sigma/\sqrt{n}$$

but,

$$\sigma = \bar{R}/d_n$$

therefore

$$A''_{.001}\bar{R} = \frac{3.09\bar{R}}{d_n} - \frac{3.09\bar{R}}{d_n\sqrt{n}}$$

i.e.

$$A''_{.001} = 3.09/d_n(1 - 1/\sqrt{n})$$

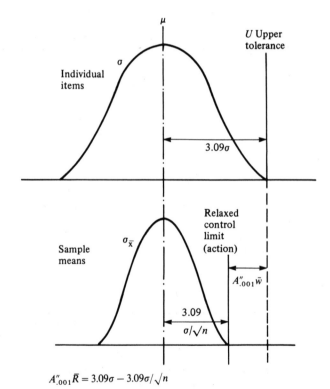

$$A''_{.001}\bar{R} = 3.09\sigma - 3.09\sigma/\sqrt{n}$$

Fig. 6.7   Relaxed control charts

Similarly, the distance between the Upper Warning Line and U is $A''_{.025}\bar{R}$, where:

$$A''_{.025} = 1/d_n(3.09 - 1.96/\sqrt{n}).$$

The values of $A''_{.001}$ and $A''_{.025}$ have been calculated for each sample size and appear in Appendix E, T, Table E3. The setting of the control limits for the relaxed mean chart is now simply:

Upper Action Line $= U - A''_{.001}\bar{R}$
Upper Warning Line $= U - A''_{.025}\bar{R}$
Lower Warning Line $= L + A''_{.025}\bar{R}$
Lower Action Line $= L + A''_{.001}\bar{R}$

If the production of 0.1% material outside tolerance is unacceptable and a lower figure is required, then the A'' constants may be adjusted accordingly. Appendix E, Table E3 also gives values for $A''_{.001}$ and $A''_{.025}$ when the percentage outside tolerance must be $< 0.01\%$.

Let us calculate relaxed mean chart limits for the steel rod cutting process, assuming that the specification for length is 125 mm to 175 mm. Firstly we must establish the precision class, $n = 4$, $\bar{R} = 10.8$ mm:

$$\text{RPI} = 2T/\bar{R} = 50/10.8 = 4.63.$$

Consultation of Table E2 indicates High Relative Precision and that relaxed control charts may be used. Assuming that we are prepared to accept 1 in 1000 rods with lengths outside the specification, then from Appendix E:

$$A''_{.001} = 0.75 \quad \text{and} \quad A''_{.025} = 1.02.$$

The relaxed mean control chart limits are:

Upper Action Line $= 175 - (0.75 \times 10.8) = 166.9$ mm
Upper Warning Line $= 175 - (1.02 \times 10.8) = 164.0$ mm
Lower Warning Line $= 125 + (1.02 \times 10.8) = 136.0$ mm
Lower Action Line $= 125 + (0.75 \times 10.8) = 133.1$ mm

The reader may like to compare these control chart limits with those for the conventional charts calculated in section 5.2:

	Conventional mean chart	*Relaxed control chart*
Upper Action Line	158.2 mm	166.9 mm
Upper Warning Line	155.2 mm	164.0 mm
Lower Warning Line	145.0 mm	136.0 mm
Lower Action Line	142.0 mm	133.1 mm

As expected, the limits on the relaxed charts are much wider than those on the conventional charts, thus allowing greater movement of process mean before adjustment.

In some cases, it may be desirable to allow the process mean to move towards one of the tolerances, e.g. the lower, but not to allow the process to drift to a higher mean. The desired control may be achieved, in such cases, by setting up mixed control charts using the relaxed lower limits and conventional upper action and warning limits. Such a mean chart could be designed to control the lengths of the steel rods.

The reader will observe that 'relaxed' range charts have not been suggested. Relaxed mean charts must always be used together with conventional range charts. Allowing the process spread to increase invalidates the calculations of relative precision and relaxed mean chart control limits.

6.5   Worked Examples in Statistical Process Control of Variables

Lathe Operation

A component used as part of a power transmission is manufactured using a lathe. Twenty samples, each of five components, are taken at half-hourly intervals and, for the most critical dimension, the grand mean is found to be 3.500″, with a normal distribution of results about the mean and a mean sample range of 0.0007″.

(a) Use this information to set up suitable control charts.
(b) If the specified tolerance is 3.499″ to 3.501″, what is your reaction? Would you consider any action necessary?
(c) Table 6.1 shows the operator's results over one day. All measurements are taken as the variation from the target mean, 3.500″, and are shown in 0.001″.
     What is your interpretation of these results?
     Do you have any comments on the process and/or the operator?

Solution

(a)   Grand Mean, $\bar{X} = 3.500''$

                             Mean Sample Range, $\bar{R} = 0.0007''$

                             Sample Size, $n = 5$

Table 6.1 Results from lathe operation

Time	1	2	3	4	5
7.30	0.2	0.5	0.4	0.3	0.2
7.35	0.2	0.1	0.3	0.2	0.2
8.00	0.2	−0.2	−0.3	−0.1	0.1
8.30	−0.2	0.3	0.4	−0.2	−0.2
9.00	−0.3	0.1	−0.4	−0.6	−0.1
9.05	−0.1	−0.5	−0.5	−0.2	−0.5

MACHINE STOPPED–TOOL CLAMP READJUSTED

10.30	−0.2	−0.2	0.4	−0.6	−0.2
11.00	0.6	0.2	−0.2	0.0	0.1
11.30	0.4	0.1	−0.2	0.5	0.3
12.00	0.3	−0.1	−0.3	0.2	0.0

LUNCH

12.45	−0.5	−0.1	0.6	0.2	0.3
1.15	0.3	0.4	−0.1	−0.2	0.0

RESET TOOL BY − 0.15

1.20	−0.6	0.2	−0.2	0.1	−0.2
1.50	0.4	−0.1	−0.5	−0.1	−0.2
2.20	0.0	−0.3	0.2	0.2	0.4

2.35   BATCH FINISHED – MACHINE RESET

4.15	1.3	1.7	2.1	1.4	1.6

Mean Chart

From Appendix B:

$A'_{.025} = 0.377$ $A'_{.001} = 0.594$

Mean Control Chart is set-up with:

Upper Action Limit $\bar{X} + A'_{.001} \bar{R} = 3.50042''$

Upper Warning Limit $\bar{X} + A'_{.02} \bar{R} = 3.50026''$

Mean $\bar{X} = 3.500''$

Lower Warning Limit $\bar{X} - A'_{.02} \bar{R} = 3.49974''$

Lower Action Limit $\bar{X} - A'_{.001} \bar{R} = 3.49958''$

Range Chart

From Appendix C:

$D'_{.999} = 0.16$

$D'_{.975} = 0.37$

$D'_{.025} = 1.81$

$D'_{.001} = 2.34$

so the Range Control Chart is set up with:

Upper Action Limit $D'_{.001} \bar{R} = 0.0016''$

Upper Warning Limit $D'_{.025} \bar{R} = 0.0013''$

Lower Warning Limit $D'_{.975} \bar{R} = 0.00026''$

Lower Action Limit $D'_{.999} \bar{R} = 0.00011''$

(b) RPI $= 2T/\bar{R} = 0.002''/0.0007'' = 2.857$
    From Appendix E, Min. RPI $(n = 5) = 2.580$

The process has medium relative precision which infers that only very few results will fall outside the tolerances, but there is little room for drift or adverse change of the process. If possible, the process should be improved. If this is not possible, the process will need to be kept strictly in control using the control charts designed.

(c) The Means and Ranges of the given results have been calculated in Table 6.2 and plotted on control charts with the limits calculated in (a) (Fig. 6.8).

Observations on the control charts

(i) There is a repeat at 7.35, but no requirement for adjustment.
(ii) The adjustment at 9.05 is justified by two consecutive results outside the same warning limit.

Table 6.2   Mean and ranges of results from Table 6.1

Time	Mean (× 0.001")	Range (× 0.001")
7.30	0.32	0.3
7.35	0.2	0.2
8.00	− 0.06	0.5
8.30	0.02	0.6
9.00	− 0.26	0.7
9.05	− 0.36	0.4
10.30	− 0.16	1.0
11.00	0.14	0.8
11.30	0.22	0.7
12.00	0.02	0.6
12.45	0.10	1.1
1.15	0.08	0.6
1.20	− 0.14	0.8
1.50	− 0.10	0.9
2.20	0.10	0.7
4.15	1.62	0.8

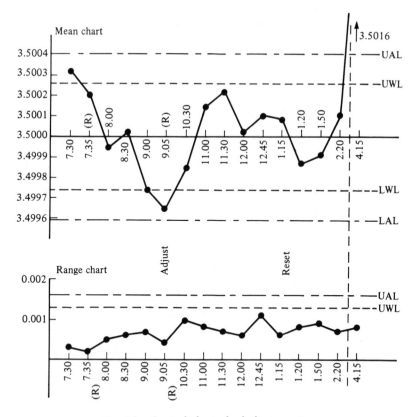

Fig. 6.8 *Control charts for lathe operation*

(iii) The re-set at 1.15 was made because five sample means were above the target mean. Assuming no drift, the estimated correction should have been the average departure from mean of the last five results, i.e. 0.11 and not 0.15. However the reset did not adversely affect control.
(iv) The whole batch was within tolerance.
 (v) At 4.15 the machine was incorrectly reset.

General conclusions
The operator's actions were correct or rational – a good operator. The machine may have been drifting upwards, possibly due to tool wear.

Control of dissolved iron in a dyestuff

Mean and range charts are to be used to maintain control on dissolved iron content of a dyestuff formulation in parts per million (ppm). After 25 subgroups of 5 measurements have been obtained.

$$\sum_{i=1}^{i=25} \bar{x}_i = 390 \quad \text{and} \quad \sum_{i=1}^{i=25} R_i = 84$$

where $\bar{x}_i$ = mean of ith subgroup

R_i = range of ith subgroup

(a)   Design the appropriate control charts.

(b)   The specification on the process requires that no more than 18 ppm dissolved iron be present in the formulation. Assuming a normal distribution and that the process continues to be in statistical control with no change in average or dispersion, what proportion of the individual measurements may be expected to exceed this specification?

Solution

$$\text{Grand Mean, } \bar{X} = \frac{\Sigma \bar{x}_i}{k} = \frac{390}{25} = 15.6 \text{ ppm}$$

$$k = \text{No. of samples} = 25$$

$$\text{Mean Range, } \bar{R} = \frac{\Sigma R_i}{k} = \frac{84}{25} = 3.36 \text{ ppm}$$

$$\sigma = \frac{\bar{R}}{d_n} = \frac{3.36}{2.326} = 1.445 \text{ ppm}$$

(d_n from Appendix B = 2.326, $n = 5$)

$$\sigma_x = \frac{\sigma}{\sqrt{n}} = \frac{1.445}{\sqrt{5}} = 0.646 \text{ ppm}$$

Mean Chart

Action Lines $= 15.6 \pm (3.09 \times 0.646)$
$\bar{X} \pm (3.096\sigma_{\bar{x}})$
$= 13.6 \text{ and } 17.6 \text{ ppm}$

Warning Lines $= 15.6 \pm (1.96 \times 0.646)$

$= 14.3 \text{ and } 16.9 \text{ ppm}$

Range Chart

Upper Action Line $= D'_{.001}\bar{R} = 2.34 \times 3.36 = 7.9 \text{ ppm}$
Upper Warning Line $= D'_{.025}\bar{R} = 1.81 \times 3.36 = 6.1 \text{ ppm}$

Alternative calculations of Mean Chart Control Lines

Action Lines
$$= \bar{X} \pm A'_{.001}\bar{R}$$
$$= 15.6 \pm (0.594 \times 3.36)$$

Warning Lines
$$= \bar{X} \pm A'_{.025}\bar{R}$$
$$= 15.6 \pm (0.377 \times 3.36)$$

$A'_{.001}$ and $A'_{.025}$ from Appendix B

(b) Specification

$$Zu = \frac{U - \bar{X}}{\sigma}$$

$$= \frac{18.0 - 15.6}{1.445} = 1.66$$

From Normal tables (Appendix A), proportion outside upper tolerance = 0.0485 or 4.85%.

Pin Manufacture

Samples are being taken from a pin manufacturing process every 15–20 minutes. The production rate is 350–400 per hour, and the specification limits on length are 0.820 and 0.840 inches. After 20 samples of 5 pins, the following information is available:

Sum of the sample means, $\displaystyle\sum_{i=1}^{i=20} \bar{x}_i = 16.68$ inches

Sum of the sample ranges, $\displaystyle\sum_{i=1}^{i=20} R_i = 0.14$ inches.

Where $\bar{x}_i$ and R_i are the mean and range of the ith sample respectively:

(a) Set up mean and range charts to control the lengths of pins produced in the future.
(b) On the assumption that the pin lengths are normally distributed, what per cent of the pins would you estimate to have lengths outside the specification limits when the process is under control at the levels indicated by the data given?
(c) Could the per cent defective be reduced to almost zero by adjusting the process average?
(d) What would happen to the per cent defective if the process average should change to 0.837 inches?
(e) What is the probability that you would observe the change in (d) on your control chart on the first sample following the change?

Solution

(a) $\displaystyle\sum_{i=1}^{i=20} \bar{x}_i = 16.88, \quad k = \text{No. of samples} = 20$

Grand Mean, $\bar{\bar{X}} = \sum \bar{x}_i/k = \dfrac{16.88}{20} = 0.834''$

Mean Range, $\bar{R} = \sum \bar{R}_i/k = \dfrac{0.14}{20} = 0.007''$

Mean Chart

Action Lines at $\bar{\bar{X}} \pm A'_{.001}\bar{R} = 0.834 \pm (0.594 \times 0.007)$

Upper A.L. $= 0.838''$

Lower A.L. $= 0.830''$

Warning Lines at $\bar{\bar{X}} \pm A'_{.025}\bar{R} = 0.834 \pm (0.377 \times 0.007)$

Upper W.L. $= 0.837''$

Lower W.L. $= 0.831''$

The A' constants are obtained from Appendix B.

Range Chart

Upper Action Line at $D'_{.001}\bar{R} \quad = 2.34 \times 0.007'' = 0.0164''$
Upper Warning Line at $D_{.025}\bar{R} = 1.81 \times 0.007'' = 0.0127''$

The D' constants are obtained from Appendix C.

(b) $\sigma = \dfrac{\bar{R}}{d_n} = \dfrac{0.007}{2.326} = 0.003''$

Upper Tolerance

$$Zu = \frac{(U - \bar{\bar{X}})}{\sigma} = \frac{(0.84 - 0.834)}{0.003} = 2$$

Therefore percentage outside upper tolerance $= 2.275\%$ (from Appendix A)

Lower Tolerance

$$Zi = \frac{(\bar{\bar{X}} - L)}{\sigma} = \frac{(0.82 - 0.834)}{0.003} = 4.67$$

Therefore percentage outside lower tolerance $= 0$
Total outside both tolerances $= 2.275\%$

(c) $2T = 0.84 - 0.82 = 0.02''$
   $6\sigma = 6 \times 0.003 = 0.018''$

$$\text{Relative Precision Index (RPI)} = \frac{2T}{R} = \frac{0.02}{0.007} = 2.86$$

i.e. Medium RPI, therefore no rejects necessary.
If $\mu = 0.83$ and $\sigma = 0.003$,

$$Zu = \frac{U - \mu}{\sigma} = \frac{\mu - L}{\sigma} = \frac{0.001}{0.003} = 3.30$$

Percentage outside tolerance $= 2 \times 0.04\% = <0.1\%$ (from Appendix A)

(d) $\quad Zu = \dfrac{0.84 - 0.837}{0.003} = 1$

Therefore percentage outside upper tolerance will increase to 15.87% (from Appendix A)

(e) $\quad \sigma_{\bar{x}} = \sigma/\sqrt{n} = \dfrac{0.003}{\sqrt{5}} = 0.0013$

Upper Warning Line (UWL)

As $\mu = $ UWL, the probability of sample point being outside
UWL $= 0.5$ (50%)

Upper Action Line (UAL)

$$Z_{UAL} = \frac{0.838 - 0.837}{0.0013} = 0.769$$

Therefore from tables, probability of sample point being outside
UAL $= 0.2206$

Thus, the probability of observing the change to $\mu = 0.837''$ on the first sample after the change is:

0.50 – outside warning line (50% or 1 in 2)
0.2206 – outside action line (22.1% or ca. 1 in 4.5)

CHAPTER 7

Other Control Charts for Variables

7.1 Introduction

As we have seen in Chapter 5, control charts may be used to maintain control of a process. They are also effective tools for analysing process capability. Numerous papers have been published on the applications and modifications of control charts. It is not possible to refer here to all the various innovations, which have filled volumes of journals. In this chapter we shall not delve into these many refinements and modifications of control charts, but concentrate on some of the most important and useful applications.

The control charts for variables, first formulated by Shewhart, make use of the arithmetic mean and the range of samples to determine whether a process is in a state of statistical control. Some control chart techniques exist which makes use of other measures.

Charts for Individuals

The simplest variable chart which may be plotted is one for individual measurements. Figure 7.1 shows measurements of lengths from a process making lithographic plates. The specification tolerances in this case are 640 mm $\pm$ 1.5 mm and these may be drawn on the chart, if the process is known to be normally distributed. When using the conventional sample mean chart the tolerances are not included, since the distribution of the means is much narrower than that of the process population, and confusion may be created if the tolerances are shown.

Where charts for means and their relationship with specification tolerances are not easily accepted or understood, or only a few measurements are available – perhaps because it is very expensive or time consuming to obtain the data – then the chart for individual item values is better than nothing. It is, however, much less satisfactory than the conventional mean chart, largely because of its relative insensitivity to

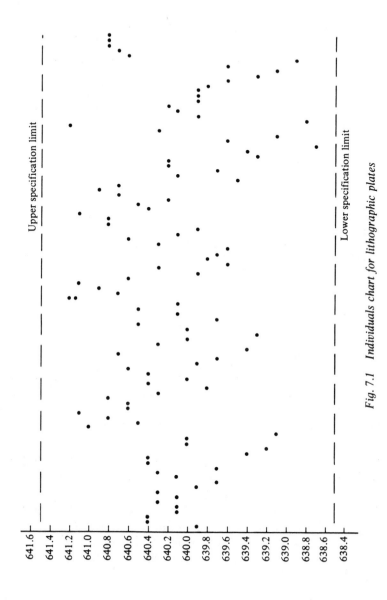

Fig. 7.1 Individuals chart for lithographic plates

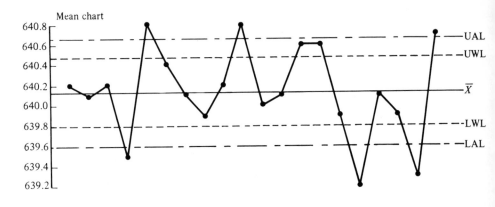

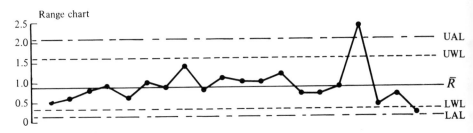

Fig. 7.2   Mean and range charts for lithographic plates

substantial changes in process average. Compare, for example, the individual chart of Fig. 7.1 with the charts for mean and range of sample size 5 in Fig. 7.2. The latter uses exactly the same data as the former, but with grouping of the results. The individual measurements and their subgroupings are given in Table 7.1. The control limits for Fig. 7.1 have been calculated using the standard method described in Chapter 5 (page 70).

What is quite clear from the control charts, that is not at all apparent from the individuals chart, is that the process is not in statistical control, that it was changing as the plates were being taken from the process. Also there is no information, from Fig. 7.1, about the spread or capability of the process. To detect changes in process spread, the individuals chart must be accompanied by a range chart, which in turn requires subgrouping of the values (minimum sub group size, $n = 2$). Alternatively, a moving range chart, described in Section 7.3, may be used in conjunction with the chart for individual values.

In general, the chart for individual measurements is inferior to other types of control chart because it gives neither a clear picture of changes

Table 7.1   Lengths of lithographic plates (mm)

Sample number	(i)	Plate (ii)	Lengths (iii)	(mm) (iv)	(v)	Sample mean (mm)	Sample range (mm)
1	639.9	640.4	640.4	640.1	640.1	640.2	0.5
2	640.3	640.1	640.3	639.9	639.7	640.1	0.6
3	640.1	640.3	639.6	640.4	640.4	640.2	0.8
4	639.4	639.2	640.0	640.0	639.1	639.5	0.9
5	641.0	640.5	640.8	641.1	640.6	640.8	0.6
6	640.6	640.8	640.3	639.8	640.4	640.4	1.0
7	640.0	640.4	640.6	639.9	639.7	640.1	0.9
8	640.7	639.4	640.3	640.0	639.3	639.9	1.4
9	640.0	640.5	639.7	641.1	640.5	640.2	0.8
10	640.1	641.2	640.7	640.9	641.1	640.8	1.1
11	640.6	639.9	640.3	639.6	639.8	640.0	1.0
12	639.7	639.6	640.3	640.6	640.1	640.1	1.0
13	639.9	640.8	640.8	641.1	640.4	640.6	1.2
14	640.5	640.2	640.7	640.9	640.7	640.6	0.7
15	639.5	640.1	639.7	640.2	640.2	639.9	0.7
16	639.3	639.4	638.7	639.6	639.1	639.2	0.9
17	640.3	641.2	638.8	639.9	640.1	640.1	2.4
18	640.2	639.9	639.9	639.9	639.8	639.9	0.4
19	639.6	639.3	639.1	639.6	638.9	639.3	0.7
20	640.6	640.7	640.8	640.8	640.8	640.7	0.2

taking place nor evidence of assignable causes of variation. An improvement is the combined individual-sample mean chart, which may show the specification tolerances and the upper and lower control limits. Such a chart, which would be provided by superimposing Figs. 7.1 and 7.2, does however increase complexity and the chances of errors in interpretation.

Mean Charts with Variable Sample Size

The mean charts described in Chapter 5 have constant sample sizes and it is desirable that, where possible, this should be so. In some situations, changes in sample sizes cannot be avoided. For example, when deliveries are being made, it is frequently impossible to control the number of batches being delivered. If one item or 'scoop' sample is to be taken from each homogenous batch, and the results plotted on a mean chart, the sample sizes will vary each time. For statistical perfection, this situation requires the calculation of different action and warning lines for each sample size. Figure 7.3 shows a mean chart with variable sample sizes and the corresponding variable control limits, which become closer to the grand mean as the sample size increases. Such a chart requires many control chart limit calculations, and careful explanation to process operators. For these

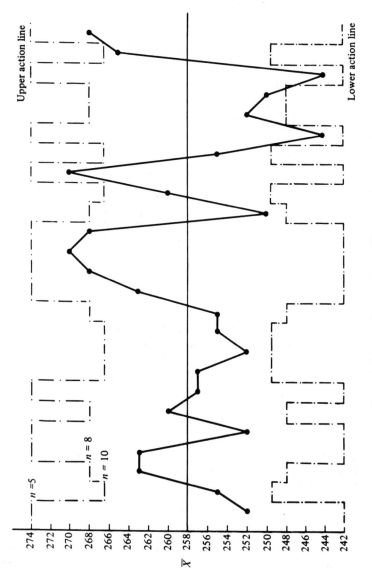

Fig. 7.3   Mean chart with variable action limits

reasons, this type of chart should be used only where it is not possible to maintain a constant sample size.

The method of calculating the variable control limits may be simplified by calculating the process standard deviation for each sample, σ_i from the formula:

$$\sigma_i = R_i/d_n$$

where,

$$R_i = \text{the sample range,}$$

$$dn = \text{Hartley's Constant for the sample size } n \text{ (see Appendix B).}$$

An estimate of the overall process standard deviation, may then be obtained by finding the average of the values of σ_i. Hence,

$$\sigma = \sum_{i=1}^{k} \sigma_i/k = \sum_{i=1}^{k} (R_i/d_n)/k$$

where $k = $ the number of samples of variable size.

This method is not precisely correct in statistical theory, but it provides an excellent working approximation. The control chart limits for each sample size may be calculated as before, namely:

Action Lines at:
$$\bar{X} \pm 3.09\sigma/\sqrt{n} \text{ and}$$

Warning Lines at:
$$\bar{X} \pm 1.96\sigma/\sqrt{n}$$

7.2 Control Charts for Median and Mid-Range

As we saw in Chapter 4, there are several measures of central tendency of variables data. An alternative to sample average is the median, and control charts for this may be used in place of mean charts. The most convenient method for producing the median chart is to plot the individual item values for each sample in a vertical line and to ring the median – the middle item value. This has been used to generate the chart shown in Fig. 7.4, which is derived from the data plotted in a different way in Fig. 7.1. The method is only really convenient for odd number sample sizes. It allows the tolerances to be shown on the chart, provided the process data is normally distributed.

The control chart limits for this type of chart are calculated from the median of sample ranges, which provides the measure of spread of the process. The sample medians and ranges for the data of Table 7.1 are shown

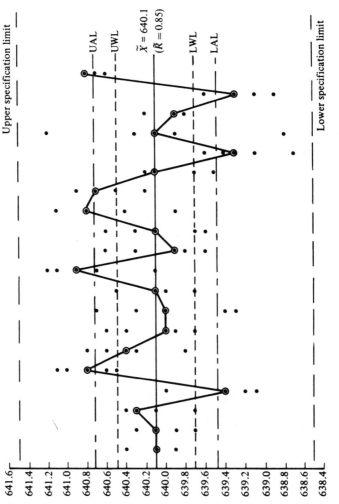

Fig. 7.4   Median chart for lithographic plates

Table 7.2   Medians and ranges of samples of lithographic plates (lengths in mm). Sample size (n) = 5

Sample number	Sample median (mm)	Sample range (mm)
1	640.1	0.5
2	640.1	0.6
3	640.3	0.7
4	639.4	0.9
5	640.8	0.6
6	640.4	1.0
7	640.0	0.9
8	640.0	1.4
9	640.1	0.8
10	640.9	1.1
11	639.9	1.0
12	640.1	1.0
13	640.8	1.2
14	640.7	0.7
15	640.1	0.7
16	639.3	0.9
17	640.1	2.4
18	639.9	0.4
19	639.3	0.7
20	640.8	0.2

Grand Median $(\tilde{X}) = 640.1$
Median Range $(\tilde{R}) = 0.85$

in Table 7.2, which also gives the Grand Median $(\tilde{X})$ – the median of the sample medians, and the Median Range $(\tilde{R})$ – the median of the sample ranges. The control limits for the median chart are calculated in a similar way to those for the mean chart, using the factors $A^m_{.001}$ and $A^m_{.025}$. Hence, median chart Action Lines appear at:

$$\tilde{X} \pm A^m_{.001}\tilde{R}$$

and the Warning Lines at

$$\tilde{X} + A^m_{.025}\tilde{R}$$

Use of the factors, which are reproduced in Appendix F, requires that the samples have been taken from a process which has a normal distribution.

A chart for medians should be accompanied by a range chart so that the spread of the process is monitored. It may be convenient, in such a case, to calculate the range chart control limits from the median sample range, $\tilde{R}$ rather than the mean range, $\bar{R}$. The factors for doing this are given in

Appendix F, and used as follows:

$$\text{Action Line at } D^m_{.001}\tilde{R}$$
$$\text{Warning Line at } D^m_{.025}\tilde{R}$$

The advantage of using sample medians over sample means is that the former are very easy to find, particularly for odd sample sizes where the method of circling the individual item values on a chart is used. No arithmetic is involved. The main disadvantage, however, is that the median does not take account of the extent of the extreme values – the highest and lowest. Thus, the medians of the two samples below are identical, even though the spread of results is obviously different. The sample means take account of this difference and provide a better measure of the central tendency.

Sample No	Item Values	Median	Mean
1	134, 134, 135, 139, 143	135	137
2	120, 123, 135, 136, 136	135	130

This failure of the median to give weight to the extreme values can be an advantage in situations where 'outlyers' – item measurements with unusually high or low values – are to be treated with suspicion.

A technique related to the median chart is the chart for midrange. The middle of the range of a sample may be determined by calculating the average of the highest and lowest values. The midrange of the sample of five 553, 555, 561, 554, 551, is:

$$\overbrace{\underbrace{561}_{\text{Highest}} + \underbrace{551}_{\text{Lowest}}}^{} \over 2 = 556$$

The central line on the midrange control chart is the median of the sample midranges $\tilde{M}$. The estimate of process spread is again given by the median of sample ranges and the control chart limits are calculated in a similar fashion to those for the median chart. Hence,

Action Lines at:

$$\tilde{M} \pm A^m_{.001}\tilde{R}$$

Warning Lines at:

$$\tilde{M} \pm A^m_{.025}\tilde{R}$$

7.3   Control Charts for Moving Average and Moving Range

An important technique for handling data which is difficult or time consuming to obtain, and therefore not available in sufficient numbers to

Table 7.3   Percentage unreacted monomer in a polymerisation process

	Time (hrs)	% Monomer		Time (hrs)	% Monomer
Day 1	0000	0.17		1600	0.20
	0400	0.24		2000	0.30
	0800	0.06	Day 5	0000	0.21
	1200	0.14		0400	0.14
	1600	0.20		0800	0.17
	2000	0.31		1200	0.28
Day 2	0000	0.13		1600	0.18
	0400	0.11		2000	0.11
	0800	0.16	Day 6	0000	0.07
	1200	0.17		0400	0.11
	1600	0.13		0800	0.12
	2000	0.16		1200	0.12
Day 3	0000	0.10		1600	0.16
	0400	0.14		2000	0.11
	0800	0.14	Day 7	0000	0.09
	1200	0.17		0400	0.11
	1600	0.15		0880	0.08
	2000	0.20		1200	0.16
Day 4	0000	0.26		1600	0.01
	0400	0.02		2000	0.15
	0800	0.19	Day 8	0000	0.18
	1200	0.18		0400	0.20

enable the use of conventional mean and range charts, is the moving average and moving range chart. In the chemical industry, for example, the nature of certain production processes and/or analytical methods causes long time intervals between consecutive results. We have already seen in this chapter that plotting of individual results offers a poor method of control, which is insensitive to changes in process average and affords little information about the spread of the process. On the other hand, waiting for several results in order to plot a mean chart may allow many tonnes of material to be produced outside specification before one point can be plotted.

In a polymerisation process, one of the important measures of quality is the impurity – unreacted monomer. Individual results are usually obtained once every four hours, with a minimum interval of two hours between results. Typical data from such a process appears in Table 7.3. Knowledge of the central limit theorem (Chapter 4, page 68) tells us that a suitable sample size is 4. The calculation of the moving average and moving range for the first three samples is shown overleaf:

Time (hrs)	Individual Result	Moving Total (n = 4)	Moving Average	Moving Range
0000	0.17			
0400	0.24			
0800	0.06			
1200	0.14	0.61	0.153	0.18
1600	0.20	0.64	0.160	0.18
2000	0.31	0.71	0.178	0.25

For each successive group of four, the earliest result is discarded and replaced by the latest. In this way it is possible to obtain and plot an 'average' and 'range' every time an individual result is obtained – in this case every four hours. The complete set of $n = 4$ moving averages and moving ranges for this data is listed in Table 7.4. These have been plotted on charts in Fig. 7.5, together with the individual results from which they were derived.

The purist statistician would require that these points be plotted at the midpoint, thus the moving average for the first four results should be placed on the chart at time 0600 hours. In practice, however, the point is usually plotted at the last result time, in this case 1200 hours. In this way the moving average and moving range charts indicate the current situation, rather than being behind time.

The moving average chart has a smoothing effect on the results compared with the individual plot. This enables trends and changes to be observed more readily. The larger the sample size the greater the smoothing effect. So a sample size of six would smooth even more the curves of Fig. 7.5. A disadvantage of increasing sample size, however, is the lag in following any trend – the greater the size of the grouping, the greater the lag. This is shown quite clearly in Fig. 7.6 in which sales data have been plotted using moving averages of three and nine individual results.

The control limits for moving average and moving range charts are derived in exactly the same way as those for conventional mean and range charts. Hence, records from the polymerisation process under consideration show, for a sample size of $n = 4$, a Grand Mean, $\bar{X}$ of 0.15%, and a Mean Range, of 0.09%, and the limits for the moving average chart are:

Actions Lines at:

$$\bar{X} \pm A'_{.001}\bar{R}$$
$$= 0.15 \pm (0.75 \times 0.09)$$
$$= 0.218 \text{ and } 0.083$$

Table 7.4   Moving averages and moving ranges for data on unreacted monomer from Table 7.3

	Time (hrs)	% Monomer	Moving total (n = 4)	Moving average	Moving range
Day 1	0000	0.17			
	0400	0.24			
	0800	0.06			
	1200	0.14	0.61	0.15	0.18
	1600	0.20	0.64	0.16	0.18
	2000	0.31	0.71	0.18	0.25
Day 2	0000	0.13	0.78	0.20	0.18
	0400	0.11	0.75	0.19	0.20
	0800	0.16	0.71	0.18	0.20
	1200	0.17	0.57	0.14	0.06
	1600	0.13	0.57	0.14	0.06
	2000	0.16	0.62	0.16	0.04
Day 3	0000	0.10	0.56	0.14	0.07
	0400	0.14	0.53	0.13	0.06
	0800	0.14	0.54	0.14	0.06
	1200	0.17	0.55	0.14	0.07
	1600	0.15	0.60	0.15	0.03
	2000	0.20	0.66	0.17	0.06
Day 4	0000	0.26	0.78	0.20	0.11
	0400	0.02	0.63	0.16	0.24
	0800	0.19	0.67	0.17	0.24
	1200	0.18	0.65	0.16	0.24
	1600	0.20	0.59	0.15	0.18
	2000	0.30	0.87	0.22	0.12
Day 5	0000	0.21	0.89	0.22	0.12
	0400	0.14	0.85	0.21	0.16
	0800	0.17	0.82	0.21	0.16
	1200	0.28	0.80	0.20	0.14
	1600	0.18	0.77	0.19	0.14
	2000	0.11	0.74	0.19	0.17
Day 6	0000	0.07	0.64	0.16	0.21
	0400	0.11	0.47	0.12	0.11
	0800	0.12	0.41	0.10	0.05
	1200	0.12	0.42	0.11	0.05
	1600	0.16	0.51	0.13	0.05
	2000	0.11	0.51	0.13	0.05
Day 7	0000	0.09	0.48	0.12	0.07
	0400	0.11	0.47	0.12	0.07
	0800	0.08	0.39	0.10	0.03
	1200	0.12	0.40	0.10	0.04
	1600	0.01	0.32	0.08	0.11
	2000	0.05	0.26	0.07	0.11
Day 8	0000	0.08	0.26	0.07	0.11
	0400	0.06	0.20	0.05	0.07

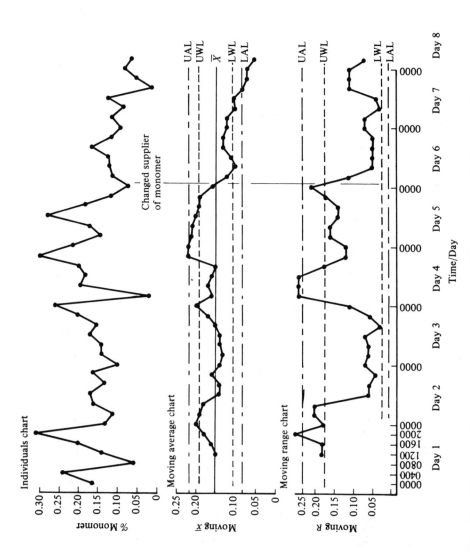

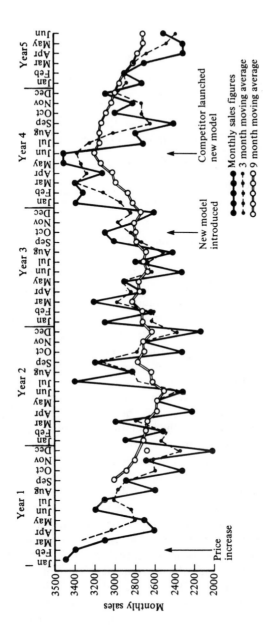

Fig. 7.6 Sales figures and moving average charts

Warning Lines at:

$$\bar{X} \pm A'_{.025}\bar{R}$$
$$= 0.15 \pm (0.476 \times 0.09)$$
$$= 0.193 \text{ and } 0.107$$

Similarly for the moving range chart:

Action Lines at:

$$D'_{.999}\bar{R} \text{ and } D'_{.001}\bar{R}$$
$$= 0.10 \times 0.09 \text{ and } 2.57 \times 0.09$$
$$= 0.009 \text{ and } 0.231$$

Warning Lines at:

$$D'_{.975}\bar{R} \text{ and } D'_{.025}\bar{R}$$
$$= 0.29 \times 009 \text{ and } 1.93 \times 0.09$$
$$= 0.026 \text{ and } 0.174$$

The factors, $A'_{.001}$, $A'_{.025}$, $D'_{.001}$, $D'_{.025}$, $D'_{.975}$, and $D'_{.999}$ are obtained from Appendices B and C as for conventional mean and range charts.

Care must be taken in the interpretation of moving average and moving range charts. Plots on or outside any of the action lines are treated in the same way as those appearing on or outside action limits on the conventional charts, and should be followed by an adjustment or investigation of the process parameters. When points first fall in the warning zone (on the warning line or between warning and action), again the interpretation is similar – either take a repeat result or increase the frequency of testing. In the case of the polymerisation process, the sampling frequency is increased to one result every two hours (the minimum). The difference between the conventional control chart and the moving average/moving range chart arises when successive plots fall in the warning zone.

The probability of two successive plots in the warning zone on a conventional mean chart is ca. $(1/40 \times 1/40) = 1/1600$, which is so low that action is taken if this occurs. For a moving average of a group of size four, however, successive points on the chart are not independent. Figure 7.7 shows how the points at 1200, 1600, 2000, and 2400 hours are related, each containing constituent results of the other three (A, B, C, D). It is only the next point at 0400 hours which comprises four completely different individual values (E, F, G, H). Consequently, action is not taken when successive points fall in the warning zone until $n + 1$, in this case five, consecutive moving average points are plotted in that region. The same applies, of course, to the interpretation of the moving range chart.

It is worth pointing out that in the example of unreacted monomer, used to illustrate moving average and moving range charts, adjustments would

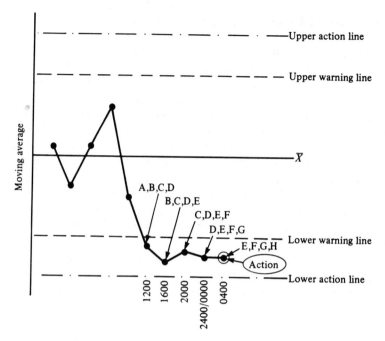

Fig. 7.7   Interpretation of moving average chart

not be made to the process to increase the impurity if points fell below the lower action and warning lines. Rather an 'action' situation should initiate an investigation into the assignable causes of the improvement. The use of any control charts in this way can be of value equal to, if not greater than, the usual search for problems.

Charts for Individuals and Moving Range

In situations where results are available at very infrequent intervals, such as once per day, it may be desirable to plot the individuals. An example outside the quality control area is data on absenteeism. The quality characteristics of bulk tanker deliveries, which may be received only once or twice per day or per week can be usefully plotted on such charts.

In order that an indication of the dispersion of the 'process' may be obtained, some sort of range chart should accompany the plot for individual results. The moving range chart, with minimum subgroup size of 2, is recommended for this type of application. The calculation of control limits has been explained in the previous description of moving range charts.

7.4   Control Charts for Standard Deviation

Range charts are commonly used to control the precision or spread of processes. Ideally, a chart for standard deviation should be used but, because of the difficulties associated with calculating and understanding standard deviation, sample range is substituted.

Significant advances in computing technology have led to the availability of cheap pocket electronic calculators with a standard deviation key. Using such calculators, experiments in Japan have shown that the time required to calculate sample range is greater than that for sigma, and the number of miscalculations is greater when using the former statistic. The conclusions of this work were that mean and standard deviation charts provide a simpler and better method of process control for variables than mean and range charts, when a calculator with standard deviation key is available.

The standard deviation chart is very similar to the range chart (see Chapter 5, page 73), the estimated standard deviation (s_i) for each sample being calculated, plotted, and compared to predetermined limits:

$$s_i = \sum_{i=1}^{n} (x_i - \bar{x})^2/(n-1)$$

Those using calculators for this computation must use the $s(n-1)$ key and not the $\sigma(n)$ key. As we have seen in Chapter 4, the sample standard deviation calculated using the 'n' formula will tend to underestimate the standard deviation of the whole process, and it is the value of $s(n-1)$ which is plotted on a standard deviation chart. The use of in the sample standard deviation is allowed for in the factors used to find the control chart limits.

Statistical theory allows the calculation of a series of constants (c_n) which enables the estimation of the process standard deviation (σ) from the average of the sample standard deviations ($\bar{s}$). The latter is the simple arithmetic mean of the sample standard deviations and provides the central line on the control chart.

$$\bar{s} = \sum_{i=1}^{k} s_i/k$$

where

$\bar{s}$ = average of the sample standard deviations

s_i = standard deviation ($n-1$ formula) of sample i

k = number of samples.

The relationship between σ and $\bar{s}$ is given by the simple ratio:

$$\sigma = \bar{s}c_n$$

where

σ = process standard deviation

c_n = a constant, dependent on sample size. Values for c_n appear in Appendix G.

The control limits on the standard deviation chart, like those on the range chart are asymmetrical, in this case about the average of the sample standard deviations ($\bar{s}$). The table in Appendix G provides four constants $B'_{.001}$, $B'_{.025}$, $B'_{.975}$ and $B'_{.999}$ which may be used to calculate the control limits for a standard deviation chart from $\bar{s}$. The table also gives the constants $B_{.001}$, $B_{.025}$, $B_{.975}$, and $B_{.999}$ which are used to find the warning and action lines from the process standard deviation, σ. The control chart limits for the control chart are calculated as follows:

Upper Action Line at $B'_{.001}\bar{s}$ or $B_{.001}\sigma$
Upper Warning Line at $B'_{.025}\bar{s}$ or $B_{.025}\sigma$
Lower Warning Line at $B'_{.975}\bar{s}$ or $B_{.975}\sigma$
Lower Action Line at $B'_{.999}\bar{s}$ or $B_{.999}\sigma$

An example should help to clarify the design and use of the chart. Let us re-examine the steel rod cutting process which we met in Chapter 5 and for which we designed mean and range charts. The data has been reproduced in Table 7.5 together with the standard deviation (s_i) for each sample of size 4. The next step in the design of a standard deviation chart is the calculation of the average sample standard deviation ($\bar{s}$). Hence:

$$\bar{s} = \frac{4.43 + 8.76 + 5.44 \dots 7.42}{25}$$

$$= 4.75$$

The process standard deviation (σ) may now be found. From Appendix G for a sample size, $n = 4$, $c_n = 1.085$ and:

$$\sigma = 4.75 \times 1.085 = 5.15$$

This is very close to the value obtained from the mean range:

$$\sigma = \bar{R}/d_n = 10.8/2.059 = 5.25$$

The control limits may now be calculated using either σ and the B constants from Appendix G or $\bar{s}$ and the B' constants:

$$\text{Upper Action Line} = 2.522 \times 4.75$$

$$\text{or} \quad 2.324 \times 5.15$$

$$= 11.97$$

Table 7.5   100 steel rod lengths as 25 samples of size 4

Sample number	Rod lengths (mm)				Sample mean (mm)	Sample range (mm)	Sample standard deviation (mm)
	(i)	(ii)	(iii)	(iv)			
1	144	146	154	146	147.50	10	4.43
2	151	150	134	153	147.00	19	8.76
3	145	139	143	152	144.75	13	5.44
4	154	146	152	148	150.00	8	3.65
5	157	153	155	157	155.50	4	1.91
6	157	150	145	147	149.75	12	5.25
7	149	144	137	155	146.25	18	7.63
8	141	147	149	155	148.00	14	5.77
9	158	150	149	156	153.25	9	4.43
10	145	148	152	154	149.75	9	4.03
11	151	150	154	153	152.00	4	1.83
12	155	145	152	148	150.00	10	4.40
13	152	146	152	142	148.00	10	4.90
14	144	160	150	149	150.75	16	6.70
15	150	146	148	157	150.25	11	4.79
16	147	144	148	149	147.00	5	2.16
17	155	150	153	148	151.50	7	3.11
18	157	148	149	153	151.75	9	4.11
19	153	155	149	151	152.00	6	2.58
20	155	142	150	150	149.25	13	5.38
21	146	156	148	160	152.50	14	6.61
22	152	147	158	154	152.75	11	4.57
23	143	156	151	151	150.25	13	5.38
24	151	152	157	149	152.25	8	3.40
25	154	140	157	151	150.50	17	7.42

$$\text{Upper Warning Line} = 1.911 \times 4.75$$
$$\text{or} \quad 1.761 \times 5.15$$
$$= 9.08$$

$$\text{Lower Warning Line} = 0.291 \times 4.75$$
$$\text{or} \quad 0.268 \times 5.15$$
$$= 1.38$$

$$\text{Lower Action Line} = 0.098 \times 4.75$$
$$\text{or} \quad 0.090 \times 5.15$$
$$= 0.46$$

Figure 7.8 shows control charts for sample standard deviation and range plotted using the data from Table 7.5. The range chart is, of course, exactly the same as that shown in Fig. 5.4. The charts are very similar and either of

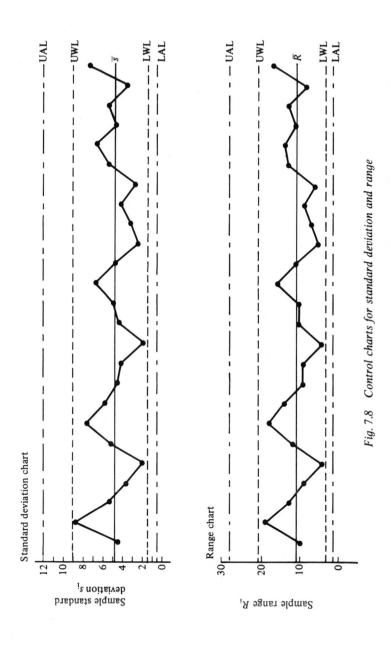

Fig. 7.8   Control charts for standard deviation and range

them may be used to control the dispersion of the process, together with the mean chart to control process average.

If the standard deviation chart is to be used to control spread, then it may be more convenient to calculate the mean chart control limits from either the average sample standard deviation ($\bar{s}$) or the process standard deviation (σ). The formulae are:

$$\text{Action Lines at:} \quad \bar{X} \pm A_{.001}\sigma$$
$$\text{or} \quad \bar{X} \pm A''_{.001}\bar{s}$$
$$\text{Warning Lines at:} \quad \bar{X} \pm A_{.001}\sigma$$
$$\text{or} \quad \bar{X} \pm A'''_{.001}\bar{s}$$

It may be recalled from Chapter 5 that the action lines on the mean chart are set at:

$$\bar{X} \pm 3.09\,\sigma/\sqrt{n}$$

hence, the constant, $A_{.001}$ must have the value:

$$A_{.001} = 3.09/\sqrt{n}$$

which for a sample size of four:

$$A_{.001} = 3.09/\sqrt{4} = 1.545$$

Similarly:

$$A_{.025} = 1.96/\sqrt{n} \qquad \text{and for } n = 4,$$
$$A_{.025} = 1.96/\sqrt{4} = 0.98$$

In the same way the values for the A''' constants may be found from the fact that:

$$\sigma = \bar{s} \times c_n$$

Hence, the action lines on the mean chart will be placed at:

$$\bar{X} \pm 3.09\,\bar{s}c_n/\sqrt{n}$$

therefore, $\qquad A'''_{.001} = 3.09 \times c_n/\sqrt{n}$

which for a sample size of four:

$$A'''_{.001} = 3.09 \times 1.085/\sqrt{4} = 1.676$$

Similarly:

$$A'''_{.025} = 1.96 \times c_n/\sqrt{n} \qquad \text{and for } n = 4,$$
$$A'''_{.025} = 1.96 \times 1.085/\sqrt{4} = 1.063$$

The constants, $A_{.001}$, $A_{.025}$, $A''_{.001}$, and $A''_{.025}$ for sample sizes $n = 2$ to $n = 25$ have been calculated and appear in Appendix B (page 232)

Using the data on lengths of steel rods in Table 7.5, we may now calculate the action and warning limits for the mean chart:

$$\bar{X} = 150.1 \text{ mm}$$
$$\sigma = 5.15 \text{ mm} \qquad \bar{s} = 4.75 \text{ mm}$$
$$A_{.001} = 1.545 \qquad A''_{.001} = 1.676$$
$$A_{.025} = 0.98 \qquad A''_{.025} = 1.063$$

Action Lines at:

$$150.1 \pm (1.545 \times 5.15)$$
$$\text{or} \quad 150.1 \pm (1.676 \times 4.75)$$
$$= \quad 158.06 \text{ mm} \quad \text{and} \quad 142.14 \text{ mm}$$

Warning Lines at:

$$150.1 \pm (0.98 \times 5.15)$$
$$\text{or} \quad 150.1 \pm (1.063 \times 4.75)$$
$$= \quad 155.15 \text{ mm} \quad \text{and} \quad 145.05 \text{ mm}$$

These values are very close to those obtained from the mean range, $\bar{R}$ in Chapter 5:

Action Lines at 158.2 mm and 142.0 mm
Warning Lines at 155.2 mm and 145.0 mm

Control Charts for Range or Standard Deviation (when Mean Charts not appropriate)

In certain types of production, measurements are made on samples taken at different stages of the process, when means of such samples are expected to vary and are not comparable. Examples of this are to be found in chemical manufacturing, where process parameters change as the raw materials are converted into products or intermediates. It may be desirable to plot the sample means against time to observe the process profile or progress of the reaction, but control limits are not usually drawn on these graphs.

Common practice in the chemical industry is for two or more analyses to be performed on each sample, which are then compared in spread of results. Conventional range charts or standard deviation charts may be used very effectively to measure the dispersion of results within each sample. The data in Table 7.6 has been plotted in this way on the range chart of Fig. 7.9. It will be observed, by an examination of the sample means in Table 7.6, that the absolute measurement of phenol concentration is changing rapidly with

Table 7.6 *Phenol concentration in a chemical process*

Time (hrs)	Phenol concentration (g/litre)		Mean	Range
	Analysis 1	Analysis 2		
0800	215.5	216.7	216.1	1.2
0815	166.3	165.4	165.9	0.9
0830	133.8	132.3	133.1	1.5
0845	111.0	111.9	111.5	0.9
0900	93.2	92.2	139.3	1.0
0915	77.6	78.9	78.3	1.3
0930	65.5	66.0	65.8	0.5
0945	52.8	51.0	51.9	1.8
1000	44.8	44.2	44.5	0.6
1015	34.7	37.7	36.2	3.0
1030	30.1	31.1	30.6	1.0
1045	26.2	28.0	27.1	1.8
1100	22.1	23.7	22.9	1.6
1115	18.0	16.0	17.0	2.0
1130	15.5	15.5	15.5	0
1145	13.4	13.2	13.3	0.2
1200	11.0	12.3	11.7	1.3
1215	10.1	8.7	9.4	1.4
1230	9.9	9.5	9.7	0.4
1245	8.7	10.4	9.6	1.7
1300	8.5	8.4	8.5	0.1
1315	7.9	8.2	8.1	0.3
1330	7.7	7.0	7.4	0.7
1345	6.4	5.7	6.0	0.7
1400	6.4	5.6	6.0	0.8

time. Figure 7.9 shows that the analytical 'process' is in control and the spread of intra-sample results is as expected from the previous data used to design the control chart.

7.5 Multi-Vari Charts

Certain quality characteristics exhibit variation which derives from more than one source. For example, if cylindrical rods are being formed, their diameters may vary from piece to piece and along the length of each rod, due to taper. Alternatively, the variation in diameters may be due in part to the ovality within each rod. Such multiple variation may be controlled using the multi-vari chart.

In the multi-vari chart, the specification tolerances are used as control limits. Sample sizes of 3 to 5 are commonly used and the results are plotted

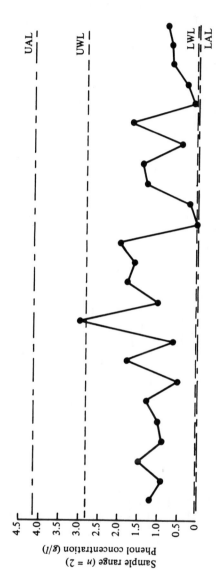

Fig. 7.9   Range chart for chemical analysis check

in the form of vertical lines joining the highest and lowest values in the sample, thereby representing the sample range. An example of such a chart used in the control of a heat treatment process is shown in Fig. 7.10 (a). The longer the lines, the more variation exists within the sample. The chart shows dramatically the effect of an adjustment, or elimination or reduction of one major cause of variation.

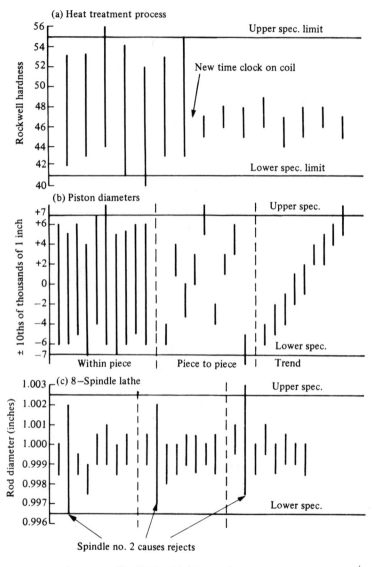

Fig. 7.10   *Multi-vari charts*

The technique may be used to analyse within piece or batch, piece to piece, or batch to batch variation. Detection of trends or drift is also possible. Figure 7.10 (b) illustrates all these applications in the measurement of piston diameters. The first part of the chart shows that the variation within each piston is very similar and relatively high. The middle section shows piece to piece variation to be high but relatively small variation within each piston. The last section of the chart is clearly showing a trend of increasing diameter, with little variation within each piece.

An extremely powerful application of the multi-vari chart in the mechanical engineering and automative industries is for trouble shooting of variation caused by the position of equipment or tooling used in the production of similar parts, for example, a multi-spindle automatic lathe, parts fitted to the same mandrel, multi-impression moulds or dies, parts held in string-milling fixtures. Use of multi-vari charts for parts produced from particular, identifiable spindles or positions can lead to the detection of the cause of faulty components and parts. Figure 7.10c shows how this can be applied to the control of ovality on an eight-spindle automatic lathe.

CHAPTER 8

Variables Control Charts in Trouble Shooting

8.1 Responsibilities

Historically, the responsibility for trouble shooting and process improvement, within a manufacturing organization, has rested with the research
and development department. In recent times, these tasks have been carried
out increasingly by people who are directly associated with the plant
operation and process control, on a day-to-day basis. What is quite clear is
that process improvement and trouble shooting should not become major
roles of the quality assurance (QA) function. QA has a minor responsibility
here and its liabilities in this area should be minimized, if not completely
eliminated.

The manufacturing or production department has the responsibility for
meeting production targets, which include those associated with the quality
of the product. It is unreasonable for manufacturing to accept responsibility
for process output, efficiency, and cost while delegating elsewhere responsibility for the quality of its output. If problems of low quantity arise during
production, whether it be the number of tablets produced per day or the
amount of herbicide obtained from a batch reactor, then these problems are
tackled without question by production personnel. Why then should
problems of – say – excessive process variation not fall under the same
umbrella?

Problems in manufacturing are rarely single-dimensional. They have at
least four dimensions:

technical (including engineering)
human
managerial
financial.

The indiscriminate involvement of QA in trouble shooting tends to polarise
attention towards the technical aspects, with the corresponding relegation
of other vital parameters. In many cases the human, managerial, and

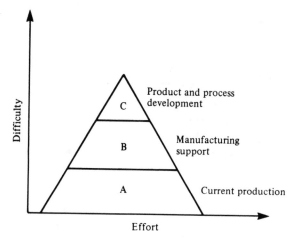

Fig. 8.1   A balanced QA function

financial dimensions have a significant bearing on the overall problem and its solution. They should not be ignored by taking a problem out of its natural environment and placing it in a 'laboratory'.

Trouble shooting implies failure. The emphasis of the 'quality' effort should be directed towards problem prevention with priorities in the areas of:

  (i) maintaining quality of current production,
 (ii) support to the line functions.
(iii) product and process development.

Fig. 8.1 shows a model of the relative size of effort against magnitude of difficulty in a balanced QA function. Fig 8.2 shows three distortions or unbalanced situations.

Quality assurance must not allow itself to become a department to be ignored when everything is running well, yet to be saddled with the responsibility for solving production quality problems as and when they arise. Associated with this practice are the dangers of QA being used as a scapegoat when explanations to senior managers are required, or being offered as a sacrificial lamb when customer complaints are being dealt with. The responsibility for quality must always lie with manufacturing and the role of QA is clearly to assist in the meeting of this responsibility. It should not be acceptable for any group within an organization to approach the quality assurance function with the question, 'We have got a problem, what are you going to do about it?'. Expert QA advice may, of course, be frequently necessary to tackle production problems.

Having described what the QA professional would regard as Utopia, we

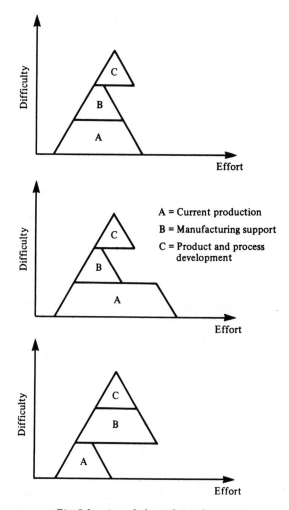

Fig. 8.2   An unbalanced QA function

must accept that the real world is inevitably less than perfect. The major problem is the one of whether manufacturing has the capabilities required to discharge its responsibilities. It is against this background that the methods in this chapter are presented.

8.2   Trouble Shooting Strategy

Trouble shooting is neither a pure science nor an art. Procedures may be presented but these will nearly always benefit from ingenuity. It is traditional to study cause and effect relationships. However, when faced with a multiplicity of potential causes, all of which involve imperfect data, it is frequently advantageous to begin with studies which identify only blocks or groups as the source of the trouble. The groups may be, for example, a complete filling line or a whole area of a manufacturing plant. Thus, the pinpointing of specific causes and effects is postponed.

An important principle to be emphasized at the outset is that a study should not aim to discover everything straight away. This is particularly important in situations where more data is obtainable quite easily.

It is impossible to set down everything which should be observed in carrying out a trouble-shooting exercise. One of the most important rules to observe is to be present when the data is being collected, at least initially. This provides the opportunity to observe possible sources of error in the acquisition of data. It may be found that improvements are necessary in the data collection method, or the type of measuring equipment. Direct observation of data collection may also suggest assignable causes which may be examined at the time. This includes the different effects due to machine changes, various suppliers, operator shifts, etc.

In trouble shooting and process improvement studies, the planning of data acquisition programmes should assist in detecting the effects of important changes. The opportunity to note possible relationships comes much more readily to the investigator who observes the data collection than the one who sits comfortably in an office chair. The further away the observer is located from the action, the less the information he obtains and the greater the doubt about the value of the information.

Effective methods of planning trouble shooting investigations have been developed over the past quarter of a century. Many of these began in the chemical, electrical, and mechanical engineering industries. The principles and practices are, however, universally applicable. Generally two approaches are available:

1. Effects of Single Factors
The effects of many single variables (e.g. temperature, voltage, agitation speed, concentration) may have been shown to have been important in other, similar studies. The procedure of altering one variable at a time is often successful, particularly in well-equipped research laboratories and pilot plants. Frequently, however, the factors which are expected to allow predictions about a new process are found to be grossly inadequate. This is especially common when a process is transferred from the laboratory or pilot plant to full-scale production. Predicted results may be obtained on some occasions but not on others, even though no known changes have been introduced. In these cases the control chart methods of Shewhart are useful to check on process stability.

2. Group Factors

A troubleshooting project may begin by an examination of the possible differences in the output quality of different operators, different machines, different filling heads, or other variables. If differences are established within such a group, experience has shown that careful study of the sources of the variation in performance will often provide important causes of those differences. Hence, the key to making adjustments and improvements is in knowing that actual differences do exist, and being able to pinpoint the sources of the differences.

It is often argued that any change in a product, process, or plant will be evident to the experienced manager. This is not the case. It is accepted that many important changes are recognized without resort to analytical studies, but the presence, and certainly the identity, of many economically important factors cannot be recognized without them.

Production processes are invariably managed by persons who combine theory, practical experience, and ingenuity. An experienced production manager will often recognize a recurring malfunctioning process by characteristic physical symptoms. As problems become more complex, however, many important changes, particularly gradual ones, cannot be recognized by simple observation and intuition, no matter how competent he or she may be as an engineer or scientist. No process is so simple, that data from it will not give added insight into its behaviour. Indeed many production processes have unrecognized complex behaviour which can only be thoroughly understood by studying data on the product which is produced. The production manager or supervisor who accepts and learns methods of statistically based investigation to support technical knowledge will be an exceptionally able person in his area.

Discussion of any trouble shooting investigation between the appropriate personnel, both technical and managerial, is essential at a very early stage. Properly planned procedures will prevent wastage of time, effort, and materials and will avoid embarrassment to those involved. It will also ensure support for implementation of the results of the study.

8.3   Use of Control Charts for Trouble Shooting

In some studies, the purpose of the data collection is to provide information on the relationships between variables. In other cases, the purpose is just to find ways to eliminate a serious problem – the data themselves, or a formal analysis of them, are of little or no consequence. The application of control charts to data can be developed in a great variety of situations and provides a simple yet powerful method of presenting and studying results. Listed here are just three advantages offered by this method:

1. Calculations are simple.
2. Errors in calculations are easily shown up.
3. Sources of assignable causes are often indicated by patterns or trends.

The use of control charts always leads to systematic programmes of sampling and measurement. The presentation of results in chart form makes the data more easily assimilated and provides a picture of the process. This is not available from a simple tabulation of the results.

The control chart method is, of course, applicable to sequences of attribute data as well as to variables data, and may well suggest causes of unusual performance. Examination of such charts, as they are plotted, may provide evidence of economically important assignable causes of trouble. The chart does not solve the problem, but it indicates when, and possibly where, to look for a solution.

The applications of control charts that we have met in Chapter 5 began with evidence that the process was in statistical control. Corrective action of some sort was then indicated when an out-of-control signal was obtained. In many trouble shooting applications, the initial results show that the process is not in statistical control and investigations must begin immediately to discover the assignable causes of variation.

It must be made quite clear that use of control charts alone will not enable the cause of trouble in a process to be identified. A thorough knowledge of the manufacturing process is also required. When this is combined with an understanding of control chart principles, then the diagnosis of causes of quality problems will be possible.

This book cannot hope to provide the intimate knowledge of every manufacturing process that is required to solve quality related problems. Guidance can only be given on the interpretation of control charts for process improvement and trouble shooting. There are many and various patterns which develop on control charts for variables when processes are not in control. What follows is an attempt to structure the patterns into various categories. The latter are not definitive, nor is the list exhaustive. The taxonomy is based on the ways in which out-of-control situations may arise and their effects on control charts for mean and range.

When points plotted on mean and range charts fall outside the control limits there is evidence that the process has changed in some way during the sampling period. This change may take three different basic forms:

- A change in the process mean, with no change in spread or standard deviation.
- A change in the process spread (standard deviation) with no change in the mean.
- A change in both the population mean and standard deviation.

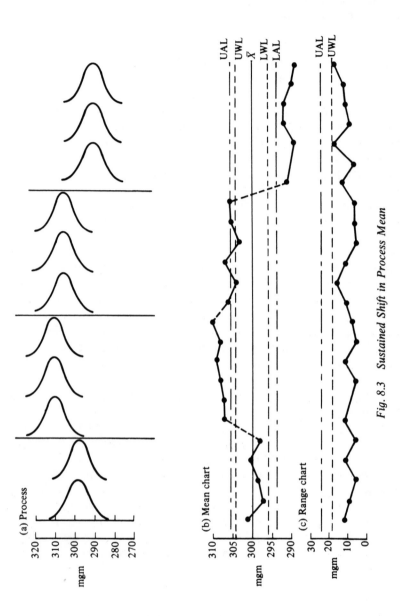

Fig. 8.3   Sustained Shift in Process Mean

These changes affect the control charts in different ways. The manner of change also causes differences in the appearance of control charts. Hence, for a constant process spread, a maintained drift in process mean will show a different pattern to frequent, but irregular changes in the mean. Therefore the list may be further divided into the following types of change:

1. Change in process mean (no change in standard deviation)
   (a) sustained shift
   (b) drift or trend – including cyclical
   (c) frequent, irregular shifts.

2. Change in process standard deviation (no change in mean)
   (a) sustained changes
   (b) drift or trends – including cyclical
   (c) frequent irregular changes.

3. Frequent, irregular changes in process mean and standard deviation

These change types are shown, together with the corresponding mean and range charts, in Figs. 8.3 to 8.9. The examples are taken from a tablet-making process in which trial control charts were being set up for a sample size of $n = 5$. In all cases, the control limits were calculated using the data which is plotted on the mean and range charts.

Sustained Shift in Process Mean (Fig. 8.3)

The process varied as shown in (a). After the first five sample plots, the process mean moved by two standard deviations. The mean chart (b) showed the change quite clearly – the next six points being above the upper action line. The change of one standard deviation, which follows, results in all but one point lying above the warning line. Finally, the out-of-control process moves to a lower mean and the mean chart once again responds immediately. Throughout these changes, the range chart (c) gives no indication of lack of control, confirming that the process spread remained unchanged.

Drift or Trend in Process Mean (Fig. 8.4)

When the process varied according to (a), the mean and range charts ((b) and (c) respectively) responded as expected. The range chart shows an in-control situation since the process spread did not vary. The mean chart response to the change in process mean of ca. two standard deviations every ten sample plots is clearly and unmistakenly that of a drifting process.

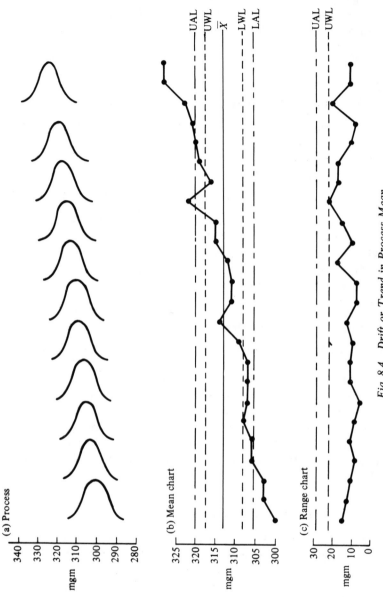

Fig. 8.4   *Drift or Trend in Process Mean*

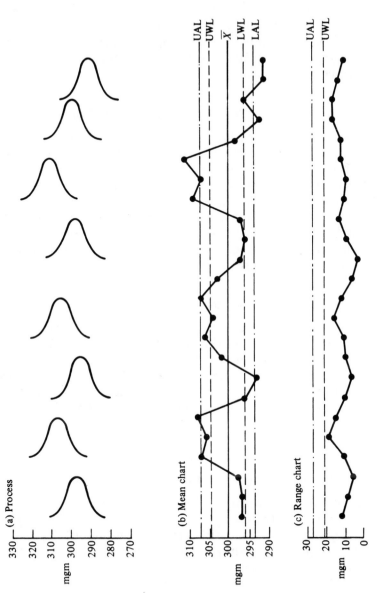

Fig. 8.5   Frequent, Irregular Shift in Process Mean

Frequent, Irregular Shift in Process Mean (Fig. 8.5)

Figure 8.5(a) shows a process in which the standard deviation remains constant, but the mean is subjected to what appear to be random changes of between one and two standard deviations every few sample plots. The mean chart (b) is very sensitive to these changes, showing an out-of-control situation and following the pattern of change in process mean. Once again the range chart (c) is in-control, as expected.

Sustained Shift in Process Standard Deviation (Figure 8.6)

The process varied as shown in (a), with a constant mean, but with changes in the spread of the process sustained for periods covering six or seven sample plots. Interestingly, the range chart (c) shows only one sample plot which is above the warning line, even though σ has increased to almost twice its original value. This effect is attributable to the fact that the range chart control limits are based upon the data itself. Hence a process showing a relatively large spread over the sampling period will result in relatively wide control chart limits. The mean chart (b) fails to detect the changes for a similar reason, and because the process mean did not change.

Drift or Trend in Process Standard Deviation (Fig. 8.7)

In (a) the pattern of change in the process results in an increase over the sampling period of two and half times the initial standard deviation. Nevertheless, the sample points on the range chart (c) never cross either of the control limits. There is, however, an obvious trend in the sample range plot and this would suggest an out-of-control process. The range chart and the mean chart (b) have no points outside the control limits for the same reason – the relatively high overall process standard deviation which causes wide control limits.

Frequent, Irregular Changes in Process Standard Deviation (Fig. 8.8)

The situation described by (a) is of a frequently changing process variability with constant mean. This results in several sample range values being near to or crossing the warning line in (c) Careful examination of (b) indicates the nature of the process – the mean chart points have a distribution which mirrors the process spread.

The last three examples, in which the process standard deviation alone is changing, demonstrate the need for extremely careful examination of control charts before one may be satisfied that a process is in a state of statistical control. Indications of trends and/or points near the control

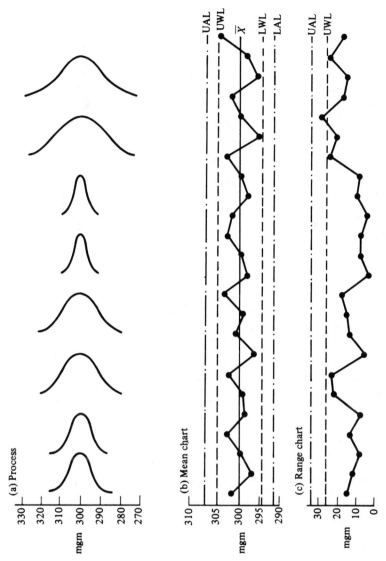

Fig. 8.6   Sustained Shift in Process Standard Deviation

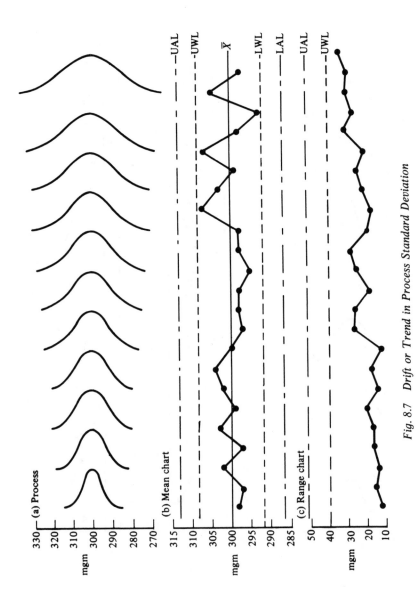

Fig. 8.7   Drift or Trend in Process Standard Deviation

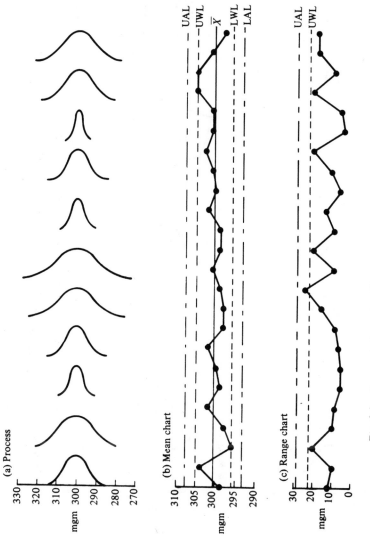

Fig. 8.8   Frequent, Irregular Changes in Process Standard Deviation

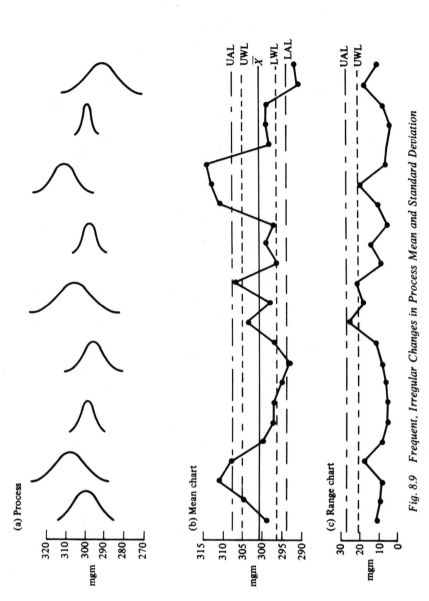

Fig. 8.9　Frequent, Irregular Changes in Process Mean and Standard Deviation

limits on the range chart may be the result of quite serious changes in variability, even though the control limits are never transgressed.

Frequent, Irregular Changes in Process Mean and Standard Deviation (Fig. 8.9)

The process varies according to (a). Both the mean and range charts ((b) and (c) respectively) are out of control and provide clear indications of a serious situation. In theory it is possible to have a sustained shift in process mean and standard deviation, or drifts or trends in both. In such cases the resultant mean and range charts would correspond to the appropriate combinations of Figs. 8.3b or 8.4b and Figs. 8.6c or 8.7c.

Process Out-of-Control

Many processes are found to be out-of-statistical control when first examined using control chart techniques. It is frequently observed that this is due to an excessive number of adjustments being made to the process, based on individual test results. This behaviour, commonly known as hunting, causes an overall increase in variability of results from the process, as shown in Fig. 8.10

If the process is initially set at the target value, μ_a and an adjustment is made

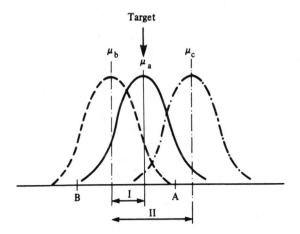

I = First adjustment based on distance of test result A
from target values $(A-\mu_a)$

II = Second adjustment based on distance of test result B
from target values (μ_b-B)

Fig. 8.10   Increase in process variability due to frequent adjustments based on individual test results

on the basis of a single test result A, then the mean of the process will be adjusted to μ_b. Subsequently, a single test result at B will result in a second adjustment of the process mean to μ_c. If this behaviour continues, the variability or spread of results from the process will be greatly increased with a detrimental effect on the ability of the process to meet the specified requirements.

Variability cannot be ignored. The simple fact that a measurement, test, or analytical method is used to generate data introduces variability. This must be taken into account and the appropriate charts for groups of data used to control processes, instead of reacting to individual results.

It is often found that range charts are in-control and indicate an inherently capable process. The saw-tooth appearance of the mean chart, however, shows the rapid alteration in the mean of the process. Hence the patterns appear in Fig. 8.5.

When a process is found to be out-of-control, the first actions must be to investigate the assignable or special causes of variability. This may require, in some cases, the charting of process parameters other than the product parameters which appear in the specification. For example, it may be that the viscosity of a chemical product is directly affected by the pressure in the reactor vessel, which in turn may be directly affected by reactor temperature. A control chart for pressure, with recorded changes in temperature, may be the first step in breaking into the complexity of the relationship involved. The important point is to ensure that all adjustments to the process are recorded and the relevant data charted.

There can be no compromise on processes which are shown to be not-in-control. The simple device of changing the charting method and/or the control limits will not bring the process into control. A proper process investigation must take place.

It has been pointed out that there are numerous potential assignable causes for processes being out-of-control. It is extremely difficult, even dangerous, to try to find an association between types of causes and patterns shown on control charts. There are clearly many causes which could give rise to different patterns in different manufacturing industries and conditions. It may be useful, however, to list some of the most common general types of assignable causes:

Labour
   fatigue
   lack of training/novices
   unsupervised
   unaware
   attitudes
   changes/improvements in skill
   rotation of shifts.

Plant/Machines
    rotation of machines
    differences in test or measuring devices
    scheduled preventative maintenance
    lack of maintenance
    badly designed equipment
    worn tools
    gradual deterioration of plant/equipment.

Processes/Methods
    unsuitable techniques of production and/or test
    untried/new production processes
    changes in inspection methods.

Materials
    merging or mixing of batches, parts, components,
        subassemblies, intermediates, etc.
    accumulation of waste products
    homogeneity
    changes in supplier/material.

Environment
    gradual deterioration in conditions
    temperature changes
    humidity
    noise
    dusty atmospheres.

It should be clear from this non-exhaustive list of the major areas that an intimate knowledge of the process is essential for the effective use of control charts in trouble shooting and process improvement programmes. The control chart, when used carefully, informs us when to look for trouble. This contributes typically 10–20% of the problem. The bulk of the work in making improvements is associated with finding where to look and which causes are operating.

CHAPTER 9

The Control of Processes Using Attributes Data – Defectives

9.1 Introduction

The quality of many products is dependent upon characteristics which cannot be measured as variables. These are called attributes and may be judged simply as either present or absent, acceptable or defective. Such properties as bubbles of air in a windscreen, the general appearance of a paint surface, the particles of contamination in a sample of polymer, and the number of clerical errors in an invoice, are all attribute parameters. It is clearly not possible to use the methods of measurement and control for variables described in Chapters 4 to 8 when addressing the problem of attributes.

The statistical behaviour of attribute data is different from that of variable data and this must be taken into account when designing process control systems for attributes. To examine which type of data distribution we are dealing with, we must know something about the product form and attribute being inspected. The following classes lead to the use of different types of control chart which are based on different statistical distributions:

1. A product in discrete units each of which can be classified as acceptable or defective, e.g. ball bearings.
2. A product in discrete units which may possess a certain number of defects, a table top for example.

When we inspect a fixed sample from the first type of product, for example 100 ball bearings, we can state how many are defective. We shall then very quickly be able to work out how many are acceptable. So in our case, if two ball bearings are found to be defective (they can also be called 'non-conformities' or 'non-conforming items'), 98 will be acceptable. This is different to the second example. If we examine a product such as a windscreen and find four defects – scratches or bubbles – we are not able to make any statements about how many scratches/bubbles are not present. This type of defect data is similar to the number of goals scored in a football match. We can only report the number of goals scored. We are unable to report how many were not.

The two types of attribute data lead to the use of two types of control chart:

1.   Number of defective chart.
2.   Number of defects chart.

These are each further split into two charts, one for the situation in which the sample size (number of units inspected) is constant, and one for samples of varying size. Hence, the collection of charts for attributes becomes:

1a.   Number of defective (np) chart – for constant sample size
  b.   Proportion defective (p) chart – for samples of varying size.
2a.   Number of defects (c) chart – for samples of same size every time
  b.   Number of defects per unit (u) chart – for varying sample size.

Process control can be exercised using these simple charts on which the number or proportion of defectives, or the number of defects or defects per unit are plotted. Before commencing to do this, however, it is absolutely vital to clarify what constitutes a defective and what is meant by a defect. No process control technique can survive the heated arguments which will surround a badly defined system. It is evident that in the study of attribute data, there will be several degrees of imperfection. The classification of defects is a subject in its own right, but it is clear that a scratch on a paintwork or table-top surface may range from a deep gouge to a slight mark, hardly visible to the naked eye. To ensure the smooth control of a process using attribute data, it is often necessary to provide representative samples, photographs, or other objective evidence to support the decision maker. These will allow the attention and the effort to be concentrated on improving the process rather than debating the issues surrounding defect levels.

9.2   Control Charts for Number Defective (np)

Consider a process which is producing ball bearings, ten per cent of which are defective. p, the proportion of defectives is 0.1. If we take a sample of one ball from the process, the chance or probability of finding a defective is 0.1, i.e. p. Similarly, the probability of finding a non-defective ball bearing is 0.90 or $(1 - p)$. For convenience we will use the letter q instead of $(1 - p)$ and add these two probabilities together:

$$p + q = 0.1 + 0.9 = 1.0$$

A total of unity means that we have present all the possibilities, since the sum of the probabilities of all the possible events must be one. This is clearly logical in the case of taking a sample of one ball bearing for there are only two possibilities – finding a defective or finding a non-defective.

If we increase the sample size to two ball bearings, the probability of finding two defectives in the sample becomes:

$$p \times p = 0.1 \times 0.1 = 0.01 = p^2$$

This is one of the first laws of probability – the multiplication law. When two or more events are required to follow consecutively, the probability of them all happening is the product of their individual probabilities. In other words, for A *and* B to happen, multiply the probabilities.

We may take our sample of two balls and find zero defectives. What is the probability of this occurrence?

$$q \times q = 0.9 \times 0.9 = 0.81 = q^2$$

Let us add the probabilities of the events so far considered:

Two defectives – probability   0.01 (p^2)
Zero defectives – probability   0.81 (q^2)
Total   0.82

It is quite obvious that we have not considered all the possible occurrences when inspecting a sample of two. There is, of course, the chance of picking out one defective and one non-defective. The probability of this occurrence is:

$$p \times q = 0.1 \times 0.9 = 0.09 = pq$$

However, the single defective may occur in the second ball bearing:

$$q \times p = 0.9 \times 0.1 = 0.09 = qp$$

This brings us to a second law of probability – the addition law. If an event may occur by a number of alternative ways, the probability of the event is the sum of the probabilities of the individual occurrences. That is, for A *or* B to happen, add the probabilities. So the probabilities of finding one defective in a sample of size 2 from this process is:

$$pq + qp = 0.09 + 0.09 = 0.18 = 2pq$$

Now, adding the probabilities:

Two defectives – probability   0.01 (p^2)
One defective – probability   0.18 $(2pq)$
No defectives – probability   0.81 (q^2)
Total probability $= 1.00$

So, when taking a sample of two from this process we can calculate the probabilities of finding one, two, or zero defective in the sample. Those who are familiar with simple algebra will recognize that the expression:

$$p^2 + 2pq + q^2 = 1$$

is an expansion of:

$$(p + q)^2 = 1$$

and this is called the Binomial expression. It may be written in a general way:

$$(p + q)^n = 1$$

where

$n =$ sample size (number of units)

$p =$ proportion of defectives in the population from which the sample is drawn

$q =$ proportion of non-defectives in the population $= (1 - p)$

To reinforce our understanding of the Binomial expression, we shall look at what happens when we take samples of size three and four:

$$n = 3$$

$$(p + q)^3 = 1$$

expands to:

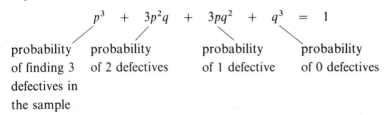

$$p^3 \quad + \quad 3p^2q \quad + \quad 3pq^2 \quad + \quad q^3 \quad = \quad 1$$

probability   probability   probability   probability
of finding 3   of 2 defectives   of 1 defective   of 0 defectives
defectives in
the sample

There is a quick way to expand any Binomial equation. Firstly, the pq terms:

In $(p + q)^n$ they become

$$p^n q^0 + p^{(n-1)}q^1 + p^{(n-2)}q^2 + p^{(n-3)}q^3 \ldots p^0 q^n \quad \text{and} \quad p^0 = q^0 = 1$$

In general, the pq term for finding x defectives in a sample size of n is:

$$p^x q^{(n-x)} = p^x(1 - p)^{(n-x)}$$

The numerical coefficients for the equation may be calculated in two ways. The longest uses Pascal's triangle:

Sample size	*Numerical coefficients in* $(p + q)^n$
$n = 1$	1 1
$n = 2$	1 2 1
$n = 3$	1 3 3 1
$n = 4$	1 4 6 4 1
$n = 5$	1 5 10 10 5 1
$n = 6$	1 6 15 20 15 6 1
	etc.

Each coefficient in the table is derived by addition of the two numbers in the line above which lie on each side of it. Thus, the expansion of $(p + q)^n$ for $n = 4$ is:

$$p^4 \quad + \quad 4p^3q \quad + \quad 6p^2q^2 \quad + \quad 4pq^3 \quad + \quad q^4$$

probability	probability	probability	probability	probability
of 4 defect-	of 3 defect-	of 2 defec-	of 1 defec-	of zero
tives in	tives	tives	tive	defectives
the sample				

A quicker solution to the numerical coefficients is given by the combination:

$$\binom{n}{x} = \frac{n!}{(n - x)!\,x!}$$

where

n = sample size

x = number of defectives

$n!$ = factorial $n = n \times (n - 1) \times (n - 2) \times (n - 3) \quad \times 1$

$x!$ = factorial $x = x \times (x - 1) \times (x - 2) \times (x - 3) \quad \times 1$

This formula gives the number of ways of selecting defectives in a sample of size n. So, for example, the numerical coefficient for the term which will give the probability of finding two defectives ($x = 2$) in a sample of size four ($n = 4$) becomes:

$$\frac{4!}{(4 - 2)! \times 2!} = \frac{4 \times 3 \times 2 \times 1}{2 \times 1 \times 2 \times 1} = 6$$

i.e. there are six ways of choosing any two from four.

The general formula for calculating the probability of finding x defectives in a sample of size n is:

$$\binom{n}{x} p^x \quad (1 - p)^{(n - x)}$$

For example, the probability $P(2)$ of finding two defectives in a sample of size 5 taken from a process producing 10% defectives may be calculated:

$$n = 5$$

$$x = 2$$

$$p = 0.1$$

$$P(2) = \frac{5!}{(5-2)!2!} \times 0.1^2 \times 0.9^3$$

$$= \frac{5 \times 4 \times 3 \times 2 \times 1}{(3 \times 2 \times 1) \times (2 \times 1)} \times 0.1 \times 0.1 \times 0.9 \times 0.9 \times 0.9$$

$$= 10 \times 0.01 \times 0.729 = 0.0729$$

This means that, on average, about seven out of one hundred samples of size 5 ball bearings, taken from the process will have two defectives in them.

It may be possible at this stage for the reader to see how this may be useful in the design of process control charts for numbers of defectives. If we can calculate the probability of exceeding a certain number of defectives in a sample, we shall be able to draw action and warning lines on charts, similar to those designed for variables in Chapter 5.

To use the probability theory we have considered so far we must know the proportion defective being produced by the process. This may be discovered by taking a reasonable number of samples – say fifty – over a typical production period, and recording the number of defectives in each. Table 9.1 lists the number of defectives found in fifty samples of size $n = 100$ taken every hour from a process producing ball-point pen cartridges. These results may be grouped into the frequency distribution of Table 9.2 and shown as the histogram of Fig. 9.1. This is clearly a different type of histogram from the symmetrical ones derived from variables data in Chapter 4.

Table 9.1 Number of defectives found in samples of 100 ball-point pen cartridges

2	2	2	2	1
4	3	4	1	3
1	0	2	5	0
0	3	1	3	2
0	1	6	0	1
4	2	0	2	2
5	3	3	2	0
3	1	1	1	4
2	2	2	3	2
3	1	1	1	1

Table 9.2   Frequency Distribution

Number of defectives in sample	Tally chart (number of samples with that number of defectives)			Frequency
0	ЦНᴛ	11		7
1	ЦНᴛ	ЦНᴛ	111	13
2	ЦНᴛ	ЦНᴛ	1111	14
3	ЦНᴛ	1111		9
4	1111			4
5	11			2
6	1			1

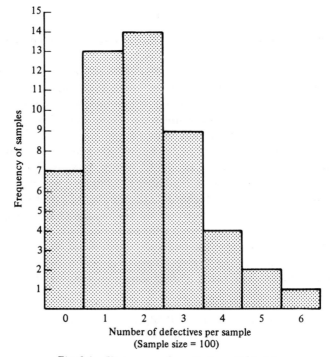

Fig. 9.1   Histogram of results from Table 9.1

The average number of defectives per sample may be calculated by adding the number of defectives and dividing the sum by the number of samples:

$$\frac{\text{Total number of defectives}}{\text{Number of samples}} = \frac{100}{50} = \text{(Average number of defectives per sample)}$$

This value is np – the sample size multiplied by the proportion defective in the process.

Hence, p may be calculated:

$$p = np/n = 2/100 = 0.02 \quad \text{or} \quad 2\%$$

We may now use the formula for the Binomial expansion to set action and warning lines for the process control chart. In the design of mean and range charts for variables we set action lines so that the probability of their being exceeded was 0.001 (one chance in 1000) unless the process changed. To set an action line with a similar probability for attribute control requires us to calculate the cumulative probabilities for x or more defectives until the 0.001 level is reached. Our ball-point pen example should clarify the explanation. Remember $n = 100$, $p = 0.02$, $(1 - p) = 0.98$.

Probability of finding 0 or more defectives, $P(\geqslant 0) = 1.0000$
Probability of finding 1 or more defectives, $P(\geqslant 1) =$
$1 -$ Probability of finding 0 defectives, $P(0)$.

$$P(0) = \frac{100!}{100!\,0!} \times 0.98^{100} = 0.1326$$

Hence, $\quad P(\geqslant 1) = 1 - 0.1326 = 0.8674$

This is considerably higher than the 0.001 level and is obviously too low for the action line. So we continue:

$$P(1) = \frac{100!}{99!\,1!} \times 0.02 \times 0.98^{99} = 0.2707$$

and $\qquad P(\geqslant 2) = 1 - P(0) - P(1)$
$$= 1 - 0.1326 - 0.2707 = 0.5967$$

If we continue this series we shall be able to complete the following table:

x or more defectives	Probability, P	
0	1.0000	
1	0.8674	
2	0.5967	
3	0.3233	
4	0.1410	
5	0.0508	
		← 0.025
6	0.0155	
7	0.0041	
		← 0.001
8	0.0009	
9	0.0002	

It is not, in fact, necessary to carry out these calculations individually. There have been many sets of statistical tables compiled* which list the probabilities derived from the expansion of the Binomial expression.

We may use the list of probabilities such as that above, or from tables, to determine where control chart limits should be set. Hence, an action line may be drawn on a number defective chart, just below 8 defectives. Similarly, a warning line may be set at a probability of 0.025 by drawing the control line between 5 and 6 defectives. Although it is not possible to find fractions of defectives in attribute sampling, ambiguity is avoided by drawing the control lines between whole numbers. The sample plots then indicate clearly when the limits have been crossed. In our example, 5 defectives found in a sample indicates normal variation whilst 6 defectives gives a warning signal that another sample should be taken immediately. In control charts for attributes it is usual to specify only the upper limits since we wish to detect an increase in defectives. Lower control lines may be drawn if required, for example to indicate when a significant process improvement has occurred, or to indicate when suspicious results have been plotted.

Figure 9.2 is an np chart on to which are plotted the data concerning the ball-point pen cartridges from Table 9.1. Since all the samples contain less defectives than the action limit and only one out of fifty enters the warning zone, the process is considered to be in statistical control. We may, therefore, reasonably assume that the process is producing an average of 2 per cent defective, and the chart may be used to control the process. The method for interpretation of control charts for attributes is exactly the same as that described for mean and range charts in Chapter 5.

Figure 9.3 shows the effect of increases in the proportion of defective pen cartridges from 2%, through 3%, 4%, 5%, 6% to 8% in steps. For each percentage defective, the run length to detection, that is the number of samples which needed to be taken before the action line is crossed following the increase in process defective, is given in the table below:

Percentage process defective	*Average run length to detection (ARL)*
3	> 10
4	> 10
5	8
6	4
8	2

Clearly, this type of chart is not as sensitive as mean and range charts for detecting changes in process defective. For this reason, the action and

Statistical Tables for Science, Engineering, Management, and Business Studies, J. Murdoch and J.A. Barnes, Macmillan, London, 2nd Edit. 1974.

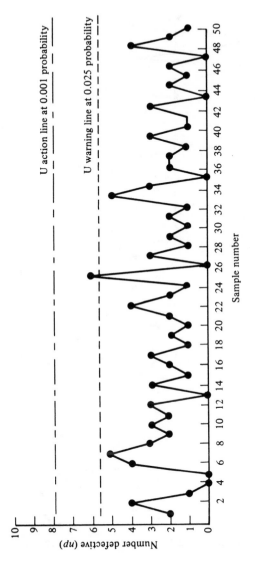

Fig. 9.2   np-chart. Number of defectives in samples of 100 ball-point pen cartridges

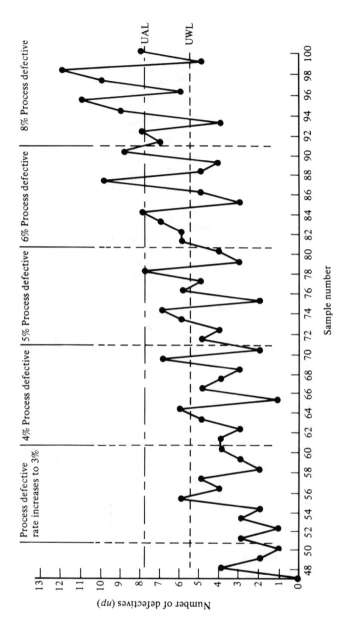

Fig. 9.3   np-chart. Defective rate of pen cartridges increasing

warning lines on attribute control charts are often set at higher probabilities. Typically, the action line is set at the one in a hundred chance of
being exceeded ($P = 0.01$), and the warning line at one in twenty ($P = 0.05$).
In our ball-point pen cartridge example, this brings the upper action line to
between 6 and 7 and the upper warning line to just below 5. A re-
examination of Fig. 9.3 with the new action and warning lines will reveal the
following changes in ARL:

Percentage Process defective	ARL changed to
3	> 10
4	9
5	4
6	3
8	1

This lowering of the action and warning lines will obviously lead to the
more rapid detection of a worsening process. It will, on the other hand,
increase the number of incorrect signals to one in twenty warning, and one
in a hundred action. Since inspection for attributes, by for example using a
go/no-go gauge, is usually less costly than the measurement of variables, an
increase in the amount of unnecessary re-sampling may be tolerated. It is
possible to set the action and warning lines on an np chart by economic
design methods, and these are described in Chapter 13.

The theoretical value of ARL may be calculated from the probability of
exceeding an action line by simply taking its reciprocal. Hence, in the pen
cartridge case, if the proportion defective is 3% ($p = 0.03$), and the action
line is set between 6 and 7, the probability of finding 7 or more defectives
may be calculated or derived from statistical tables as 0.0312 ($n = 100$). We
can now work out the average run length to detection:

$$ARL\,(3\%) = 1/P(\geqslant 7) = 1/0.0312 = 32$$

For a process producing 5% defectives, the ARL for the same sample size
and control chart is:

$$ARL\,(5\%) = 1/P(\geqslant 7) = 1/0.234 = 4$$

The ARL is always quoted to the nearest integer.

9.3 Control Charts for Attributes in the USA

The practice in the USA is to set only one set of outer limits at three
standard deviations either side of the average number defective. This will
not, however, set the control limits at or near to 0.001 probability, since

the distribution of results is not Normal – it is not even symmetrical (see Fig. 9.1). It will be found that use of the American formula usually sets the limits at a probability of about 0.01.

The standard deviation (σ) for a Binomial distribution is given by the formula for a frequency distribution:

$$\sigma = \sqrt{np(1-p)}$$

We can show that this is true by calculating σ using the conventional formula:

$$\sigma = \sqrt{\frac{\Sigma f x^2}{\Sigma f} - \bar{x}^2}$$

and comparing the result with that obtained from the new formula. Table 9.3 shows the data from Tables 9.1 and 9.2 being used to give the value of $\Sigma f x^2$. The calculation of σ now becomes:

$$\sigma = \sqrt{(300/50) - 4}$$
$$= 1.41$$

Use of the quicker formula gives the same result:

$$\sigma = \sqrt{100 \times 0.02 \times 0.98} = 1.4$$

Now, the American upper control limit (UCL) may be calculated:

$$UCL = np + 3\sqrt{np(1-p)}$$
$$= 2 + 3\sqrt{100 \times 0.02 \times 0.98}$$
$$= 6.2, \text{ i.e. between 6 and 7}$$

This result is the same as that obtained by setting the upper action line at a probability of 0.01 using Binomial tables.

Table 9.3

Number of defectives (x)	Frequency (f)	x^2	fx^2
0	7	0	0
1	13	1	13
2	14	4	56
3	9	9	81
4	4	16	64
5	2	25	50
6	1	36	36
	$\Sigma f = 50$		$\Sigma f x^2 = 300$

The reader may consider that the American formula offers a simpler method of calculating the upper action line. If so, a similar method may be employed to calculate the upper warning line. This will be set at two standard deviations above the average number defective:

$$UWL = np + 2\sqrt{np(1-p)}$$
$$= 2 + 2\sqrt{100 \times 0.02 \times 0.98}$$
$$= 4.8, \text{ i.e. between 4 and 5}$$

Again this gives the same result as that derived from using the Binomial expression to set the warning line at 0.05 probability.

To summarize then, control charts for number defective are less sensitive to slight changes in the process than charts for variables. This usually leads to the setting of control limits at probabilities higher than those associated with mean and range charts, typically:

Upper Action Line at 0.01 probability (1 in 100)
Upper Warning Line at 0.05 probability (1 in 20).

This may usually be achieved by using the simple American method and formulae. The latter method will be particularly attractive when using a sample size which does not appear in the usual Binomial tables. In these cases it is also possible to make use of the Poisson distribution as an approximation of the Binomial (see section 10.4).

9.4   Control Charts for Proportion Defective (p)

In cases where it is not possible to maintain a constant sample size for attribute control, the p-chart or proportion defective chart may be used. It is, of course, possible and quite acceptable to use the p-chart instead of the np-chart even when the sample size is constant. However, plotting directly the number of defectives in each sample onto an np-chart is usually more convenient and simple than having to calculate the proportion defective. There is also a difference in complexity of design and inter-pretation.

The data required for the design of a p-chart is very similar to that for an np-chart, the only addition being the variation in number inspected in each sample. Table 9.4 shows the results from the inspection of twenty-four samples of engine control assemblies taken daily. The sample sizes vary from 405 to 2360. For each sample, the proportion defective has been calculated:

$$p_i = x_i/n_i$$

Table 9.4   Results from the inspection of engine control assemblies with varying sample sizes

Sample number	Sample size	Number of rejects	Proportion defective
1	1135	10	0.009
2	1405	12	0.009
3	805	11	0.014
4	1240	16	0.013
5	1060	10	0.009
6	905	7	0.008
7	1345	22	0.016
8	980	10	0.010
9	1120	15	0.013
10	540	13	0.024
11	1130	16	0.014
12	990	9	0.009
13	1700	16	0.009
14	1275	14	0.011
15	1300	16	0.012
16	2360	12	0.005
17	1215	14	0.012
18	1250	5	0.004
19	1205	8	0.007
20	950	9	0.009
21	405	9	0.022
22	1080	6	0.006
23	1475	10	0.007
24	1060	10	0.009

where p_i is the proportion defective in sample i

x_i is the number of defectives in sample i

n_i is the size (number of items) of the ith sample.

As with the np-chart, the first step in the design of a p-chart is the calculation of the average proportion defective ($\bar{p}$):

$$\bar{p} = \sum_{i=1}^{k} x_i \left/ \sum_{i=1}^{k} n_i \right.$$

where k is the number of samples,

then: $\sum_{i=1}^{k} x_i$ is the total number of defective items

$\sum_{i=1}^{k} n_i$ is the total number of items inspected

For the control assemblies:

$$\bar{p} = 280/27,930 = 0.010$$

Control Chart Limits

If a constant sample size is being inspected, the p control chart limits would remain the same for each sample. So, for example, if we have a constant sample size of $n = 100$, and obtain an average proportion defective, $p = 0.01$ we can use the simplified American method to calculate an upper action line at ca. 0.01 probability and an upper warning line at ca. 0.05 probability. This will avoid the use of the Binomial statistical tables and further calculations.

$$\text{For proportion defective, } \sigma = \sqrt{np(1-p)}/n$$
$$= \sqrt{p(1-p)}/\sqrt{n}$$
$$UAL = \bar{p} + 3\sqrt{\bar{p}(1-\bar{p})}/\sqrt{n}$$
$$UWL = \bar{p} + 2\sqrt{\bar{p}(1-\bar{p})}/\sqrt{n}$$

The results for $n = 100$, $\bar{p} = 0.01$ are:

$$UAL = 0.01 + 3\sqrt{0.01 \times 0.99}/\sqrt{100}$$
$$= 0.040$$
$$UWL = 0.01 + 2\sqrt{0.01 \times 0.99}/\sqrt{100}$$
$$= 0.030$$

When samples of varying sizes are being used to plot p-charts, the control limits change and unique limits should be calculated for each sample size. However, for practical purposes, an average sample size ($\bar{n}$) may be used to calculate action and warning lines and these are acceptable when the individual sample sizes vary from $\bar{n}$ by no more than 25% each way. For sample sizes outside this range, separate control limits must be calculated.

The next stage then in the calculation of control limits for the p-chart with varying sample sizes is to determine the average sample size ($\bar{n}$) and the range 25% either side:

$$\bar{n} = \sum_{i=1}^{k} n_i/k$$

Range of sample sizes with constant
control chart limits $= \bar{n} \pm 0.25\bar{n}$

For our control assemblies:

$$\bar{n} = 27{,}930/24 = 1{,}164$$
$$\text{Range of sample size} = 1{,}164 \pm (0.25 \times 1{,}164)$$
$$= 873 \quad \text{to} \quad 1455$$

For sample sizes within that range, the control chart limits may be calculated:

$$\text{UAL} = \bar{p} + 3\sqrt{\bar{p}(1-\bar{p})}/\sqrt{\bar{n}}$$
$$= 0.01 + 3\sqrt{0.01 \times 0.99}/\sqrt{1,164}$$
$$= 0.019$$

$$\text{UWL} = \bar{p} + 2\sqrt{\bar{p}(1-\bar{p})}/\sqrt{\bar{n}}$$
$$= 0.01 + 2\sqrt{0.01 \times 0.99}/\sqrt{1.164}$$
$$= 0.016$$

Control limits for samples numbers 3, 10, 13, 16, and 21 must be calculated individually as these fall well outside the range 873 to 1455:

$$\text{UAL} = \bar{p} + 3\sqrt{\bar{p}(1-\bar{p})}/\sqrt{n}$$
$$\text{UWL} = \bar{p} + 2\sqrt{\bar{p}(1-\bar{p})}/\sqrt{n}$$

Table 9.5 shows the detail of the calculations involved and the resulting action and warning lines. Figure 9.4 shows the *p*-chart plotted with the varying action and warning lines. It is evident that the design, calculation, plotting, and interpretation of *p*-charts requires more care than that normally associated with *np*-charts.

The process involved in the manufacture of the engine control assemblies is clearly out of control – the proportion defective in sample 10 is higher than the corresponding action line. An investigation is required to discover the assignable or special causes of this poor performance, and the *p*-charts

Table 9.5   Calculation of p-chart limits for sample sizes outside the range 873 to 1455

General formulae:
$$UAL = \bar{p} + 3\sqrt{\bar{p}(1-\bar{p})}/\sqrt{n}$$
$$UWL = \bar{p} + 2\sqrt{\bar{p}(1-\bar{p})}/\sqrt{n}$$
$$\bar{p} = 0.010 \sqrt{\bar{p}(1-\bar{p})} = 0.0995$$

Sample number	Sample size	$\sqrt{\bar{p}(1-\bar{p})}/\sqrt{n}$	UWL	UAL
3	805	0.0035	0.017	0.021
10	540	0.0043	0.019	0.023
13	1700	0.0024	0.015	0.017
16	2360	0.0020	0.014	0.016
21	405	0.0049	0.020	0.025

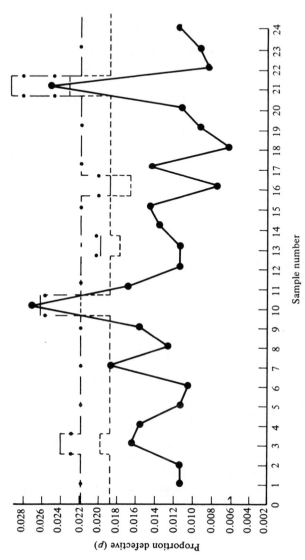

Fig. 9.4 p-chart. Proportion of defective engine control assemblies

Table 9.6   Lower control limits on the p-chart for engine control assemblies

General Formulae:

$$LWL = \bar{p} - 2\sqrt{\bar{p}(1 - \bar{p})}/\sqrt{n}$$

$$LAL = \bar{p} - 3\sqrt{\bar{p}(1 - \bar{p})}/\sqrt{n}$$

$$\bar{p} = 0.01 \sqrt{\bar{p}(1 - \bar{p})} = 0.0995$$

Sample number	Sample size	$\sqrt{\bar{p}(1-p)}/\sqrt{n}$	LWL	LAL	
All except below	1164 (n̄)	0.0029	0.004	0.001	
3	805	0.0035	0.003	− 0.0005	(i.e. 0)
10	540	0.0043	0.001	0	(− ve)
13	1700	0.0024	0.005	0.003	
16	2360	0.0020	0.006	0.004	
21	405	0.0049	0	0	(− ve)

must not be used for control purposes until they have been found and corrected. After correction the process may be re-examined and, if found to be in statistical control, the re-calculated *p*-chart used to control the process.

The lower control chart limits may also be calculated and drawn on the chart. They are set at 2 and 3 σ below the process average defective. Sample points falling below the lower action line also indicate a process which is out of control. Lower control limits are frequently omitted to avoid the need to explain to operating personnel why a very low proportion defectives is classed as being out-of-control. When the *p*-chart is to be used by quality control personnel and production management, however, the lower limits are used to indicate when an investigation should be instigated to discover the cause of an unusually good performance. This may also indicate how it may be repeated. The lower control limits for the engine control assembly process are given in Table 9.6. A re-examination of Fig. 9.4 will show that none of the sample points falls below the lower action lines.

CHAPTER 10

The Control of Processes Using Attributes Data – Defects

10.1   Control Charts for Number of Defects (c)

The control charts for attributes considered so far have applied to cases in which a random sample of definite size is selected and inspected. In these cases the following information is known:

(i)   the number of defectives in the sample
(ii) the number of non-defectives in the sample.

In the process control of attributes, there are situations where the number of defects can be counted, but there is no information about the number of defects which are not present. Examples of these include the number of imperfections on a painted door, errors in a typed document, and the number of faults in a length of woven carpet. In these cases the Binomial distribution does not apply because there is no value of n for the expression: $(p + q)^n$.

The distribution which does apply to this type of problem is the Poisson, named after the Frenchman who first described it in the nineteenth century. Because there is no fixed sample size when counting the number of defects, theoretically the number could tail off to infinity. Any distribution which does this must include something of the Exponential distribution and the constant e. This contains the element of fading away to nothing since its value is derived from the formula:

$$e = \frac{1}{0!} + \frac{1}{1!} + \frac{1}{2!} + \frac{1}{3!} + \frac{1}{4!} + \frac{1}{5!} \cdots \frac{1}{\infty!}$$

If the reader cares to work this out the value, $e = 2.7183$ is obtained.

The equation for the Poisson distribution includes the value of e and looks rather formidable at first. The probability of observing x defects in a given unit is given by the equation:

$$P(x) = e^{-\bar{c}}(\bar{c}^x/x!)$$

where

e = exponential constant, 2.7183
$\bar{c}$ = average number of defects per unit being produced by the process.

The reader who would like to see a simple derivation of this formula should refer to the excellent book, 'Facts from Figures' by M.J. Moroney (Pelican, Reprinted 1983).

So the probability of finding three bubbles in a windscreen from a process which is producing them with an average of one bubble present is given by:

$$P(3) = e^{-1} \times \frac{1^3}{3 \times 2 \times 1}$$

$$= \frac{1}{2.7183} \times \frac{1}{6} = 0.0613$$

As with the Binomial distribution, it is not necessary to calculate probabilities in this way, since statistical tables containing the information have been compiled. These have been reproduced in Appendix H as cumulative Poisson probabilities, which enable the direct calculation of the action and warning lines for the control chart for number of defects – the so-called c-chart.

In a coachwork paint process, the number of defects – scratches and small indentations – on each identical unit are being counted. Table 10.1 shows the number of defects which have been found on inspecting fifty randomly selected units over a 24-hour period. The total number of defects is 159 and, therefore, the average number of defects, $\bar{c}$ is given by:

$$\bar{c} = \sum_{i=1}^{k} c_i/k$$

Table 10.1   Number of defects on each unit of painted coachwork (50 samples)

4	2	6	3	6
2	4	1	4	3
1	3	5	5	1
3	0	2	1	3
2	6	3	2	2
4	2	4	0	4
1	4	3	4	2
5	1	5	3	1
3	3	4	2	5
7	5	2	8	3

where c_i is the number of defects on the ith unit and k is the number of units examined.

In this example,

$$\bar{c} = 159/50 = 3.2$$

Consultation of the cumulative Poisson probability tables (Appendix H) shows the following:

x or more defectives	Probability, P	
6	0.1054	
		←—0.05
7	0.0446	
8	0.0168	
		←—0.01
9	0.0057	
10	0.0018	

This table may be used to set an upper action line at 0.01 probability and a warning line at 0.05 probability of being exceeded. The values will be:

UAL between 8 and 9

UWL between 6 and 7

c-Chart Design in the USA

Just as the Americans have simplified the design of np and p charts, they have streamlined the calculation of the 'upper control limit' (UCL) for the c-chart. Once again the UCL is set at three standard deviations above the average number of defects.

The standard deviation of a Poisson distribution is very simply the square root of the process average. Hence, in the case of defects,

$$\sigma = \sqrt{\bar{c}}$$

and for our coachwork painting process:

$$\sigma = \sqrt{3.2} = 1.79$$

The UCL may now be calculated:

$$UCL = \bar{c} + 3\sqrt{\bar{c}}$$

$$= 3.2 + 3\sqrt{3.2}$$

$$= 8.57 \text{ i.e. between 8 and 9}$$

Thus, the result obtained for UCL by this method is the same as that for the

UAL at 0.01 probability using a Poisson distribution. In the same way, an upper warning line may be calculated:

$$UWL = \bar{c} + 2\sqrt{\bar{c}}$$
$$= 3.2 + 2\sqrt{3.2}$$
$$= 6.78 \text{ i.e. between 6 and 7}$$

Figure 10.1, which is a plot of the 50 coachwork inspection results used to design the c-chart, shows that the process is in statistical control, with an average of 3.2 defects on each unit. If this chart is now used to control the process, we may examine what happens over the next 25 samples, taken over a period of 12 hours. Figure 10.2 is the c-chart plot of the results.

When sample number 9 shows eight defects on the unit being inspected, this signals a warning and another sample is taken immediately. Sample 10 shows that the process has drifted out of control and results in an investigation to find the assignable cause. In this case, the paint spray nozzle was suspected and cleaning of the equipment was carried out. An immediate resample after restart of the process shows the process to be back in control. It continues to remain in that state for at least the next 14 samples.

As with all types of control chart, an improvement in quality and productivity is often observed after the introduction of the c-chart. The confidence of having a good control system, which derives as much from knowing when to leave the process alone as when to make adjustments, leads to more stable processes, less variation, and less interruptions from unecessary alterations.

10.2   Control Charts for Number of Defects Per Unit (*u*)

We saw in the previous section how the c-chart applies to the number of defects in a single unit of product, such as a table, a length of cloth, the hull of a boat, a windscreen, or the surface of an area of paint or other finish. It is not always possible, however, in this type of inspection to maintain a constant sample size or unit of material inspected. The length of pieces of cloth inspected, for instance, may vary. At other times, it is desirable to have a larger sample size than one unit. This is certainly the case if the average defects per unit falls below one. If, for example, the value of c in the painted coachwork process had fallen to 0.5, the values plotted on the chart would be mostly 0 and 1, with an occasional 2 or 3. Control of such a process by a whole number c-chart would be nebulous.

The u-chart is suitable for controlling this type of process, as it measures

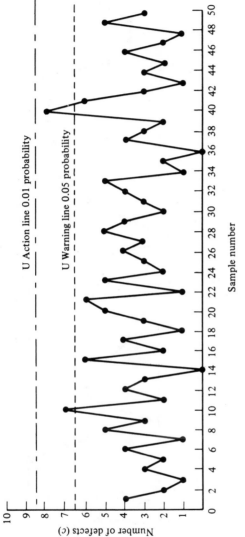

Fig. 10.1   c-chart. Coachwork paint inspection

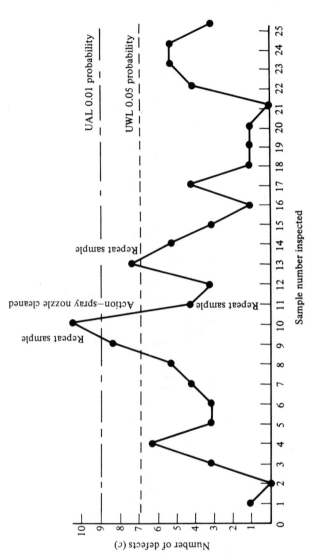

Fig. 10.2   c-chart. Coachwork paint inspection

the number of defects or non-conformities per inspection unit. The sample size can, therefore, vary. In the case of inspection of cloth or other surfaces, the area examined may be allowed to vary and the u-chart will show the number of defects per unit area, e.g. per square metre. The statistical theory behind the u-chart is very similar to that for the c-chart. An example of u-chart design should help to explain the usefulness of the technique.

Consider a process which is producing turbine blades for use in jet engines. Each blade has no less than seventeen measurements made on it. If manually plotted mean and range charts are introduced to control this process, the production operators may spend all their time plotting graphs! Examination of previous inspection records shows that the number of blades examined during each batch manufactured has varied from batch to batch. In this case we shall not examine the variables data in detail, although that would be essential at some stage to establish that the process was capable of achieving the required tolerances. Instead we shall use the data in attribute form. This conversion is quite easily achieved by comparing each measurement made with the design tolerance and deciding whether it is inside or outside specification – acceptable or not acceptable. Table 10.2 shows the number of measurements outside specification in each

Table 10.2   Number of defects (measurements out of specification) on turbine blades

Batch no.	Number of blades in sample	Number of defects in sample	Number of defects per unit (u)
1	85	40	0.47
2	88	82	0.96
3	92	95	1.03
4	83	78	0.94
5	78	125	1.60
6	75	50	0.67
7	80	105	1.31
8	72	35	0.49
9	80	72	0.90
10	92	85	0.92
11	75	68	0.91
12	81	77	0.95
13	43	75	1.74
14	80	46	0.58
15	125	120	0.96
16	120	105	0.88
17	155	250	1.61
18	81	152	1.88
19	45	17	0.38
20	50	43	0.86

sample from twenty different batches. The sample sizes vary from batch to batch. The number of 'defects' per unit in each case has also been calculated.

The design of the u-chart is similar to the design of the p-chart for proportion defective. The control lines will vary for each sample size, but for practical purposes may be kept constant if sample sizes remain within 25% either side of the average sample size, $\bar{n}$. From Table 10.2, $\bar{n}$ may be calculated:

$$\bar{n} = \sum_{i=1}^{k} n_i/k$$

where

$$n_i = \text{the size of the ith sample}$$

$$k = \text{the number of samples}$$

$$\bar{n} = 1680/20 = 84$$

25% either side of this value gives the range 63 to 105. The first 12 batches are within this range.

As in the p-chart, it is necessary to calculate the process average defect rate. In this case we introduce the symbol $\bar{u}$:

$$\bar{u} = \text{Process average defects per unit}$$

$$= \frac{\text{Total number of defects}}{\text{Total number of items inspected}}$$

$$= \sum_{i=1}^{k} x_i / \sum_{i=1}^{k} n_i$$

where

$$x_i = \text{the number of defects in sample } i.$$

Hence, $\bar{u} = 1720/1680 = 1.02$ measurements per blade outside specification.

The control chart limits for the first twelve batches may now be set, using the short American method, at 3 and 2 standard deviations from the process average. The defects found per unit will follow a Poisson distribution, the standard deviation σ of which is the square root of the process average. Hence, for the first twelve batches:

$$\text{UAL} = \bar{u} + 3 \sqrt{\bar{u}} / \sqrt{\bar{n}}$$

$$= 1.02 + (3\sqrt{1.02}/\sqrt{84})$$

$$= 1.02 + 0.33 = 1.35$$

$$\mathrm{UWL} = \bar{u} + 2\sqrt{\bar{u}}/\sqrt{\bar{n}}$$
$$= 1.02 + (2\sqrt{1.02}/\sqrt{84})$$
$$= 1.02 + 0.22 = 1.24$$

Control chart limits for batches 13, 15, 16, 17, 19, and 20 are shown in Table 10.3.

Figure 10.3 shows the defects per unit results from Table 10.2 plotted on the u-chart. There are several points above the upper action line and the process is clearly not in statistical control. In this situation it would be prudent, before proceeding to detailed and possibly expensive investigations, to do the following:

(i) ensure that the data was valid
     were the measurements carried out correctly?
     was a calibrated micrometer with known variability used?
     has the measurement system changed?
     has the data been edited or altered in any way?
(ii) ensure that all calculations and graphs are correct
     are the values of $\bar{u}$ and $\bar{n}$ correct?
     have the sample defects per unit values been determined correctly?
     have the control chart limits been calculated accurately and drawn precisely on the chart?
     have the sample results been plotted correctly?

If after examination of these points an out-of-control condition is still demonstrated, the process must be investigated to determine the assignable

Table 10.3   Calculation of u-control chart limits for sample sizes
outside the range 63–105

General formulae:
$$UAL = \bar{u} + 3\sqrt{\bar{u}}/\sqrt{n}$$
$$UWL = \bar{u} + 2\sqrt{\bar{u}}/\sqrt{n}$$
$$\bar{u} = 1.02$$

Sample number	Sample size	$\sqrt{\bar{u}}/\sqrt{n}$	UWL	UAL
13	43	0.154	1.33	1.48
15	125	0.090	1.20	1.29
16	120	0.092	1.20	1.30
17	155	0.081	1.18	1.26
19	45	0.151	1.32	1.47
20	50	0.143	1.31	1.45

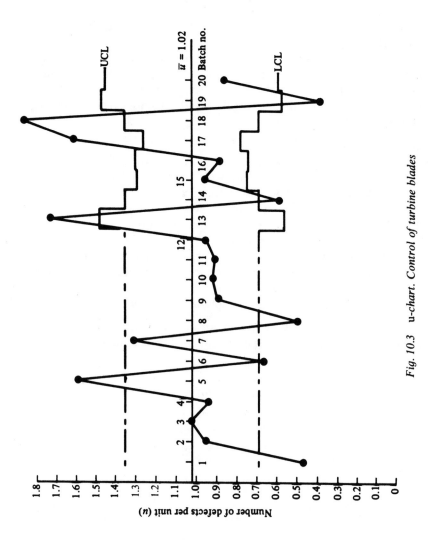

Fig. 10.3   u-chart. Control of turbine blades

causes. When discovered the causes must be corrected and, if possible, prevented from recurring. The problem solving techniques, such as the Pareto and cause and effect analyses described in Chapter 3 should be helpful. Assuming that the major assignable causes have been identified and corrected, the initial control chart limits may be recalculated, excluding the points associated with these causes. The remainder of the historical data may then be checked against the revised limits to ensure that no other points indicate the presence of further assignable causes.

In cases such as the measurement of turbine blades, the preliminary study with historical data may be complicated by the passage of time and confounded by causes or symptoms that come and go. All that can be recommended is that the analysis is carried out as systematically as possible under the circumstances. If the historical data show or, following correction of assignable causes, can be made to show consistent performance with in the trial control limits, the charts may be extended and used for future control of the process.

10.3 Improvements in Process Capability

When the process is in statistical control, the remaining average level of defects per unit will represent the capability of the process. This level reflects the presence of random causes of variation. To improve process capability requires a systematic investigation of the whole process system – not just a diagnostic examination of particular causes of lack of control. This places demands upon management to direct action towards improving such contributing factors as:

- operator performance, training, and knowledge
- machine performance, reliability, and maintenance
- material suitability, conformance, and grade.

A philosophy of never ending improvement is necessary to make inroads into process capability improvement.

It is often difficult to make progress in process improvement programmes when only attribute data is being used. One rarely finds that some form of variable data is unavailable or cannot be obtained with a little effort and expense. The extra cost associated with providing data in the form of measurements may well be trivial compared with the savings than can be derived by reducing process variability.

10.4 Approximations to Assist in Process Control of Attributes

This section is primarily intended for the reader who does not wish to accept the American short method of calculating control chart limits for sampling of attributes, but would like to set action and warning lines at known levels of probability.

The Poisson Approximation

The Poisson distribution is very easy to use. The calculation of probabilities is relatively simple and, as a result, concise tables (Appendix H) which cover many situations are readily obtainable. The Binomial distribution, on the other hand, is somewhat tedious to handle since it requires a different set of calculations to be performed for each sample size, n.

The Poisson can be used to approximate the Binomial under certain conditions. Let us examine a particular case and see how the two distributions perform. We are taking samples of size 10 from a pottery process which is producing on average one per cent defectives. Expansion of the Binomial expression, $(0.01 + 0.99)^{10}$ or consultation of the statistical tables will give the following probabilities of finding 0, 1, 2, and 3 defectives:

Number of defectives in sample of 10	Binomial probability of finding that number of defectives
0	0.9044
1	0.0913
2	0.0042
3	0.0001

There is virtually no chance of finding more than three defectives in the sample. The reader may be able to appreciate these figures more easily if we imagine that we have taken 10,000 of these samples of 10. The results should look like this:

Number of defectives in sample of 10	Number of samples out of 10,000 which have that number of defectives
0	9044
1	913
2	42
3	1

We can calculate the average number of defectives per sample:

$$\frac{\text{Average number of}}{\text{defectives per sample}} = \frac{\text{Total number of defectives}}{\text{Total number of samples}}$$

$$= \frac{913 + (42 \times 2) + 3}{10{,}000}$$

$$= \frac{1{,}000}{10{,}000} = 0.1$$

The quicker way of calculating this, of course, is to multiply the sample size by the proportion defective, i.e. np:

$$np = 10 \times 0.01 = 0.1$$

Now, in the Poisson distribution we must use the average number of defectives, $\bar{c}$ to calculate the probabilities. Hence in the approximation we let:

$$\bar{c} = np = 0.1$$

so:

$$e^{-\bar{c}}(\bar{c}^x/x!) = e^{-np}((np)^x/x!) = e^{-0.1}(0.1^x/x!)$$

and we find that the probabilities of finding defectives in the sample of 10 are:

Number of defectives in sample of 10	*Poisson probability of finding that number of defectives*	*Number of samples out of 10,000 which have that number of defectives*
0	0.9048	9048
1	0.0905	905
2	0.0045	45
3	0.0002	2

The reader will observe the similarity of these results to those obtained using the Binomial distribution.

$$\frac{\text{Average number of}}{\text{defectives per sample}} = \frac{905 + (45 \times 2) + (2 \times 3)}{10{,}000}$$

$$= \frac{1{,}001}{10{,}000} = 0.1001$$

We may now compare the calculations for the standard deviation of these results by the two methods:

Binomial $\quad \sigma = \sqrt{np(1-p)} = \sqrt{10 \times 0.01 \times 0.99} = 0.315$

Poisson $\quad \sigma = \sqrt{\bar{c}} = \sqrt{np} = \sqrt{10 \times 0.01} \quad\quad = 0.316$

The results are very similar because $(1 - p)$ is so close to unity that there is hardly any difference between the formulae for σ. This brings us to the conditions under which the approximation holds. The Binomial can be approximated by the Poisson when:

$$p \leqslant 0.10$$
$$\text{and} \quad np \leqslant 5$$

The Normal Approximation

It is also possible to provide an approximation of the Binomial distribution by the Normal curve. This applies as the proportion defective, p approaches 0.5 (50%) which, hopefully, is not very often in a quality control situation. It is, of course, valid in the case of coin tossing where the chance of obtaining a head in an unbias coin is 1 in 2. The number of heads obtained if 20 coins are tossed 10,000 times has been calculated from the Binomial in Table 10.4. The results are plotted on a histogram in Fig. 10.4. The corresponding Normal curve has been superimposed on to the histogram. It is clear that, even though the probabilities were derived from a Binomial distribution, the results are virtually Normally distributed and that we may use Normal tables to calculate probabilities.

Table 10.4   Number of heads obtained from coin tossing

Number of heads in tossing 20 coins	Probability (Binomial $n = 20$, $p = 0.5$)	Frequency of that number of heads if 20 coins are tossed 10,000 times
2	0.0002	2
3	0.0011	11
4	0.0046	46
5	0.0148	148
6	0.0370	370
7	0.0739	739
8	0.1201	1201
9	0.1602	1602
10	0.1762	1762
11	0.1602	1602
12	0.1201	1201
13	0.0739	739
14	0.0370	370
15	0.0148	148
16	0.0046	46
17	0.0011	11
18	0.0002	2

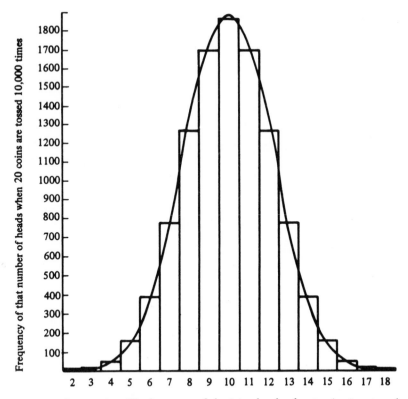

Fig. 10.4   Coin tossing. The frequency of obtaining heads when tossing twenty coins

An example illustrates the usefulness of this method. Suppose we wish to find the probability of obtaining 14 or more heads when 20 coins are tossed. Using the Binomial:

$$P(\geqslant 14) = P(14) + P(15) + P(16) + P(17) + P(18)$$

$$\text{(there is zero probability of finding more than 18)}$$

$$= 0.0370 + 0.0148 + 0.0046 + 0.0011 + 0.002$$

$$= 0.0577$$

Using the Normal tables:

$$\mu = np = 20 \times 0.5 = 10$$

$$\sigma = \sqrt{np(1-p)} = \sqrt{20 \times 0.5 \times 0.5} = 2.24$$

Since the data must be continuous for the normal curve to operate, the probability of obtaining 14 or more heads is considered to be from 13.5 upwards.

The general formulae for the z factor is:

$$z = \frac{x - 0.5 - np}{\sigma}$$

Now,

$$z = \frac{14 - 0.5 - 10}{2.24} = 1.563$$

and from the Normal tables (Appendix A) the probability of finding 14 or more heads is 0.058.

The normal curve is an excellent approximation to the Binomial when p is close to 0.5 and the sample size n is 10 or more. If n is very large then, even when p is quite small, the Binomial distribution becomes quite symmetrical and is well approximated by the Normal curve. Obviously the nearer p becomes to 0.5, the smaller n may be for the Normal approximation to be applied.

CHAPTER 11

Cumulative Sum Charts

11.1 Introduction

In Chapters 5 to 10 we have considered Shewhart control charts for variables and attributes, named after the man who first described them in the 1920s. The basic rules for the operation of these charts concern predominantly the interpretation of each sample plot. Investigative and possibly corrective action is taken if an individual sample point falls outside the action lines, or if two consecutive plots appear in the warning zone – between warning and action lines. A repeat sample is usually taken immediately after a point is plotted in the warning zone. Guidelines have been set down in Chapter 5 for the detection of trends and runs above and below the average value but, essentially, process control by Shewhart charts considers each point as it is plotted. There are alternative control charts which consider more than one sample result.

The moving average and moving range charts described in Chapter 7 take into account part of the previous data, but the technique which uses all the information available is the cumulative sum or CUSUM method. This type of chart was developed in Britain in the 1950s and is one of the most powerful management tools available for the detection of trends and slight changes in data.

The advantage of plotting the cusum chart in highlighting small but persistent changes may be seen by an examination of some simple attribute data. Samples of fifty ($n = 50$) lithographic plates from a continuous production process are being taken every half-hour and examined for imperfections – edge burrs, marks, scratches, squareness – and each plate classified as acceptable or reject. Table 11.1 shows the results following the inspection of forty samples of 50 plates. Looking at the figures alone will not give the reader any clear picture of the behaviour of the process. Figure 11.1 is an *np* chart (see Chapter 9) on which the results have been plotted. The sample points have not been connected in any way, but the control limits have been calculated from the Binomial distribution at 0.01 probability

Table 11.1   Number of defective lithographic plates in samples of size 50

Sample number	Number defective	Sample number	Number defective	Sample number	Number defective	Sample number	Number defective
1	1	11	3	21	2	31	1
2	4	12	4	22	1	32	4
3	3	13	2	23	2	33	1
4	5	14	3	24	3	34	3
5	4	15	7	25	1	35	1
6	3	16	3	26	2	36	5
7	6	17	5	27	6	37	5
8	3	18	1	28	0	38	2
9	2	19	3	29	5	39	3
10	5	20	3	30	2	40	4

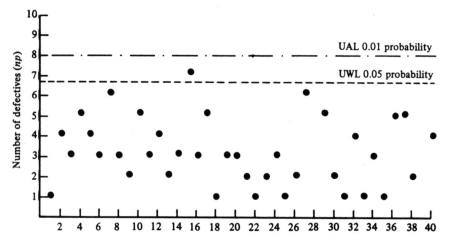

Fig. 11.1   Number defective chart for attributes (lithographic plates)

(Upper Action Line) and 0.05 probability (Upper Warning Line). The average number of defectives (np) is approximately three. The process is obviously in statistical control since none of the sample points lie outside the action line and only one of the forty results is in the warning zone. It is difficult to see from this chart any significant changes in the process.

An improvement on this presentation can be made by simply joining up the sample points and drawing a line at 3 which corresponds to the average number defective, np (Fig. 11.2). Even this does not signal clearly a change, but careful examination will reveal that the level of defectives per sample is higher between sample numbers 2 and 17 than that between 18 and 40. However, we are still looking at individual sample points.

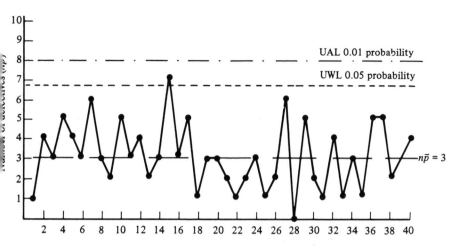

Fig. 11.2   *Number defective chart showing process average and connected sample plots*

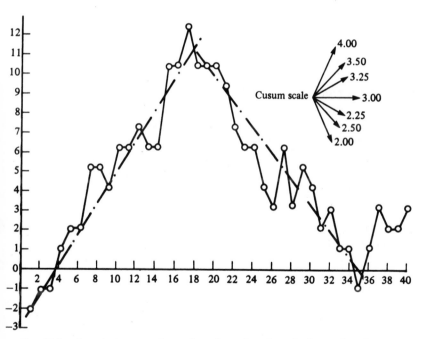

Fig. 11.3   *Cumulative sum chart of attribute data from ligthographic plate process*

Table 11.2   Cumulative sum values of data from Table 11.1 (np = 3)

Sample number	Number defective	Cusum score, Sr	Sample number	Number defective	Cusum score, Sr
1	− 2	− 2	21	− 1	9
2	1	− 1	22	− 2	7
3	0	− 1	23	− 1	6
4	2	1	24	0	6
5	1	2	25	− 2	4
6	0	2	26	− 1	3
7	3	5	27	3	6
8	0	5	28	− 3	3
9	− 1	4	29	2	5
10	2	6	30	− 1	4
11	0	6	31	− 2	2
12	1	7	32	1	3
13	− 1	6	33	− 2	1
14	0	6	34	0	1
15	4	10	35	− 2	− 1
16	0	10	36	2	1
17	2	12	37	2	3
18	− 2	10	38	− 1	2
19	0	10	39	0	2
20	0	10	40	1	3

In Figure 11.3 the same data are plotted as cumulative sums on a cusum chart. The calculations necessary to achieve this are extremely simple and are shown in Table 11.2. The average number of defectives, 3 has been subtracted from each sample result and the residues cumulated to give the cusum 'Score', Sr for each sample. Values of Sr are plotted on the chart. The difference in defective levels is shown dramatically. It is clear, for example, that from the beginning of the chart up to and including sample 17, the level of defectives is on average higher than 3, since the cusum plot has a positive slope. Between samples 18 and 35 the average defective level has fallen and the cusum slope becomes negative. Is there an increase in defective level commencing again over the last five samples? Recalculation of the average number of defectives over the two main ranges gives:

Sample numbers (inclusive)	Total number of defectives	Average number of defectives (np) per sample
1–17	63	3.7
18–35	41	2.3

This confirms that the signal from the cusum chart was valid. The task now begins of diagnosing the assignable cause of this change. It may be, for example, that the persistent change in defect level is associated with a labour shift changeover. Other factors, such as a change in material supplier, may be responsible. Only careful investigation will confirm or reject these suggestions. The main point is that the change was identified because the cusum chart takes account of past data.

Cusum charts are useful for the detection of short- and long-term changes and trends. Their interpretation requires care because it is not the actual cusum score which signifies the change, but the overall slope of the graph. For this reason the method is often more suitable as a management technique than for use on the shop floor. Production operatives will require careful training and supervision if cusum charts are to replace conventional mean and range charts or attribute charts at the point of manufacture.

The method of cumulating differences and plotting them has great application in many fields of management control. The emphasis in this book will be on the use of cusums in quality management, but they provide powerful monitors in such areas as:

forecasting – actual v. forecasted sales
absenteeism ⎫
production levels⎬ detection of slight changes
plant breakdowns – maintenance performance

and many others in which data must be used to signify changes.

11.2 Simple Cusum Charts for Variables

The interpretation of cusum charts is concerned with the assessment of gradients or slopes of graphs. Careful design of the charts is, therefore, necessary so that the appropriate sensitivity to change is obtained.

The calculation of the cusum score, Sr, is very simple and may be represented by the formula:

$$Sr = \sum_{i=1}^{r} (x_i - t)$$

where Sr is the cusum score of the rth sample

x_i is the result from the individual

sample i (x_i may be a sample mean, $\bar{x}_i$)

t is called the target value

The choice of the value of t is dependent upon the application of the technique. In the attribute example we considered earlier, t was given the value of the average number of defective plates per sample over forty samples. In a forecasting application, t may be the forecast for any particular period. In the manufacture of tablets, *t* may be the target weight or the centre of a specification tolerance band. It is clear that the choice of the *t* value is crucial to the resulting cusum graph. If the graph is always showing a positive slope, the data is constantly above the target or reference quantity. A high target will result in a continuously negative or downward slope.

As we are interested in the slope of a cusum plot the control chart design must be primarily concerned with the choice of its vertical and horizontal scales. This matter is particularly important for variables if the cusum chart is to be used in place of Shewhart charts for sample-to-sample process control at the point of manufacture.

In the design of conventional mean and range charts for variables data, we set control limits at certain distances from the process average. These corresponded to multiples of the standard error of the means, $\sigma_{\bar{x}}$. Hence, the warning lines were set approximately $2\sigma_{\bar{x}}$ from the process average and the action lines at approximately $3\sigma_{\bar{x}}$ (Chapter 5). We shall use this convention in the design of cusum charts for variables, not in the setting of control limits, but in the calculation of vertical and horizontal scales.

When we examine a cusum chart, we would wish that a major change – such as a change of $2\sigma_{\bar{x}}$ in sample mean – shows clearly, yet not so obtusely that the cusum graph is oscillating wildly following normal variation. This requirement may be met by arranging the scales such that a shift in sample mean of $2\sigma_{\bar{x}}$ is represented on the chart by ca. 45° slope. This is shown in Fig. 11.4. It requires that the distance along the horizontal axis which represents one sample plot is approximately the same as that along the vertical axis representing $2\sigma_{\bar{x}}$. An example should clarify the explanation.

In Chapter 5, we examined a process manufacturing steel rods. Data on rod lengths taken from 25 samples of size four had the following characteristics:

$$\text{Grand or Process Mean Length, } \bar{X} = 150.1 \text{ mm}$$
$$\text{Mean Sample Range, } \qquad \bar{R} = 10.8 \text{ mm}$$

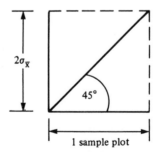

Fig. 11.4   Slope of cusum chart for a change of $2\sigma_{\bar{x}}$ in sample mean

We may use our simple formula from Chapter 5 to provide an estimate of the process standard deviation, σ:

$$\sigma = \bar{R}/d_n$$

where d_n is Hartley's Constant

$= 2.059$ for sample size $n = 4$

Hence, $\sigma = 10.8/2.059 = 5.25$ mm

This value may in turn be used to calculate the standard error of the means:

$$\sigma_{\bar{x}} = \sigma/\sqrt{n}$$

$$\sigma_{\bar{x}} = 5.25\sqrt{4} = 2.625$$

$$\text{and } 2\sigma_{\bar{x}} = 2 \times 2.625 = 5.25 \text{ mm}$$

We are now in a position to set the vertical and horizontal scales for the cusum chart. Assume that we wish to plot a sample result every 1 cm along the horizontal scale (abscissa) – the distance between each sample plot is 1cm.

To obtain a cusum slope of ca. 45° for a change of $2\sigma_{\bar{x}}$ in sample mean, 1 cm on the vertical axis (ordinate) should correspond to the value of $2\sigma_{\bar{x}}$ or thereabouts. In the steel rod process, $2\sigma_{\bar{x}} = 5.25$ mm. No one would be happy plotting a graph which required a scale 1cm = 5.25mm, so it is necessary to round up or down. Which shall it be?

Guidance is provided on this matter by the scale ratio test. The value of the scale ratio is calculated as follows:

$$\text{Scale Ratio} = \frac{\text{Linear distance between plots along abscissa}}{\text{Linear distance representing } 2\sigma_{\bar{x}} \text{ along ordinate}}$$

The value of the scale ratio should lie between 0.8 and 1.5. In our example if we round the ordinate scale to 1 cm = 4 mm, the following scale ratio will result:

Linear distance between plots along abscissa $= 1$ cm

Linear distance representing $2\sigma_{\bar{x}}$ (5.25 mm) $= 1.3125$ cm

and scale ratio $= 1$ cm$/1.3125$ cm $= 0.76$

This is outside the required range and the chosen scales are unsuitable. Conversely, if we decide to set the ordinate scale at 1 cm = 5 mm, the scale ratio becomes 1 cm$/1.05$ cm $= 0.95$, and the scales chosen are acceptable. Having designed the cusum chart for variables, it is usual to provide a key showing the slope which corresponds to changes of two and three $\sigma_{\bar{x}}$ (Fig. 11.5). A similar key may be used with simple cusum charts for attributes. This is shown in Fig. 11.3.

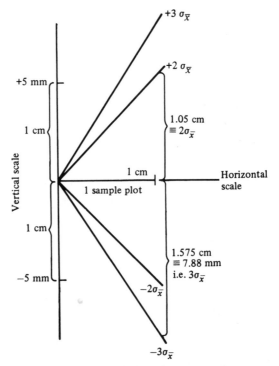

Fig. 11.5   Scale key for cusum plot

We may now use the cusum chart to analyse data. Table 11.3 shows the sample means from 30 groups of four steel rods, which were used in plotting the mean chart of Fig. 5.6 (Chapter 5). The process average of 150.1 mm has been subtracted from each value and the cusum values calculated. The latter have been plotted on the previously designed chart to give Fig. 11.6.

If the reader compares this chart with the corresponding mean chart certain features will become apparent. Firstly, an examination of sample plots 11 and 12 on both charts will demonstrate that the mean chart more readily identifies large changes in the process mean. This is by virtue of the sharp 'peak' on the chart and the presence of action and warning limits. The cusum chart depends on comparison of the gradients of the cusum plot and the key. Secondly, the zero slope or horizontal line on the cusum chart between samples 12 and 13 shows what happens when the process is perfectly in control. The actual cusum score of sample 13 is still high at 19.80, even though the sample mean (150.0 mm) is almost the same as the reference value (150.1 mm).

The care necessary when interpreting cusum charts is shown again by sample plot 21. On the mean chart there is a clear indication that the

Table 11.3 Cusum values of sample means (n = 4) for steel rod cutting process

Sample number	Sample mean, $\bar{x}$ (mm)	$(\bar{x} - t)$ mm (t = 150.1 mm)	Sr
1	148.50	− 1.60	− 1.60
2	151.50	1.40	− 0.20
3	152.50	2.40	2.20
4	146.00	− 4.10	− 1.90
5	147.75	− 2.35	− 4.25
6	151.75	1.65	− 2.60
7	151.75	1.65	− 0.95
8	149.50	− 0.60	− 1.55
9	154.75	4.65	3.10
10	153.00	2.90	6.00
11	155.00	4.90	10.90
12	159.00	8.90	19.80
13	150.00	− 0.10	19.70
14	154.25	4.15	23.85
15	151.00	0.90	24.75
16	150.25	0.15	24.90
17	153.75	3.65	28.55
18	154.00	3.90	32.45
19	157.75	7.65	40.10
20	163.00	12.90	53.00
21	137.50	− 12.60	40.40
22	147.50	− 2.60	37.80
23	147.50	− 2.60	35.20
24	152.50	2.40	37.60
25	155.50	5.40	43.00
26	159.00	8.90	51.90
27	144.50	− 5.60	46.30
28	153.75	3.65	49.95
29	155.00	4.90	54.85
30	158.50	8.40	63.25

process has been over-corrected and that the lengths of rods are too short. On the cusum plot the negative slope between plots 20 and 21 indicates the same effect, but it must be understood by all who use the chart that the rod length should be increased, even though the cusum score remains high at over 40 mm. The power of the cusum chart is its ability to detect persistent changes in the process mean and this is shown by the two parallel trend lines drawn on Fig. 11.6. More objective methods of detecting significant changes, using the cusum chart, are introduced in section 11.4 and described fully in Chapter 12.

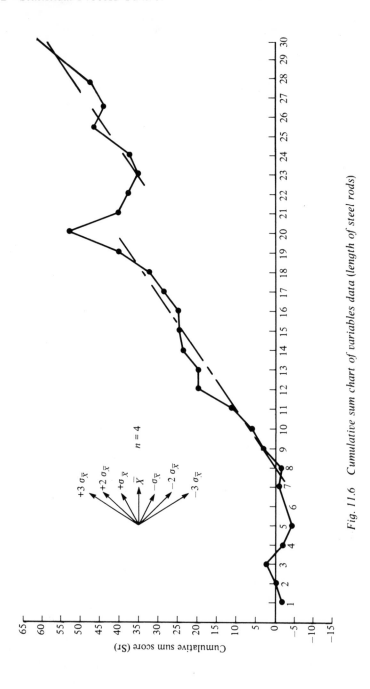

Fig. 11.6   Cumulative sum chart of variables data (length of steel rods)

11.3   Product Screening and Pre-selection

Cusum charts can be used in categorizing production output. This may be for the purposes of selection for different further processes or assembly operations, or for dispatch to different customers with slightly varying requirements. To perform the screening or selection, the cusum chart is divided into different sections of average process mean by virtue of changes in the slope of the cusum plot. Consider, for example, the cusum chart for rod lengths in Fig. 11.6. The first 8 samples may be considered to represent a stable period of production and the average process mean over that period is easily calculated:

$$\sum_{i=1}^{8} \bar{x}_i/8 = t + (S_8 - S_0)/8$$

$$= 150.1 + (-1.55 - 0)/8 = 149.91$$

The first major change in the process occurs at sample 9 when the cusum chart begins to show a positive slope. This continues until sample 12. Hence, the average process mean may be calculated over that period:

$$\sum_{i=9}^{12} x_i/4 = t + (S_{12} - S_8)/4$$

$$= 150.1 + (19.8 - (-1.55))/4 = 155.44$$

In this way the average process mean may be calculated from the cusum score values for each period of significant change.

For samples 13 to 16, the average process mean is:

$$\sum_{i=13}^{16} x_i/4 = t + (S_{16} - S_{12})/4$$

$$= 150.1 + (24.9 - 19.8)/4 = 151.38$$

For samples 17 to 20:

$$\sum_{i=17}^{20} x_i/4 = t + (S_{20} - S_{16})/4$$

$$= 150.1 + (53.0 - 24.9)/4 = 157.13$$

For samples 21 to 23:

$$\sum_{i=21}^{23} x_i/3 = t + (S_{23} - S_{20})/3$$

$$= 150.1 + (35.2 - 53.0)/3 = 144.17$$

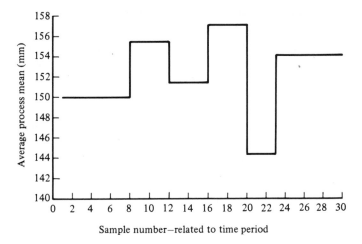

Fig. 11.7   *Manhattan diagram – average process mean with time*

For samples 24 to 30:

$$\sum_{i=24}^{30} x_i/7 = t + (S_{30} - S_{23})/7$$
$$= 150.1 + (63.25 - 35.2)/7 = 154.11$$

This information may be represented on a Manhattan diagram, named after its appearance. Such a graph has been drawn for the above data in Fig. 11.7. It shows clearly the variation in average process mean over the timescale of the chart.

11.4   Introduction to Decision Procedures

Cusum charts are used to detect when changes have occurred. The extreme sensitivity of cusum charts, which was shown in the previous sections, needs to be controlled if unnecessary adjustments to the process and/or stoppages are to be avoided. The largely subjective approaches examined so far are not very satisfactory. It is desirable to use objective decision rules, similar to the control limits on Shewhart charts, to indicate when significant changes have occurred. Several methods are available, but two in particular have practical application in industrial situations, and these are described here. They are:

(i)   V-masks
(ii) Decision Intervals

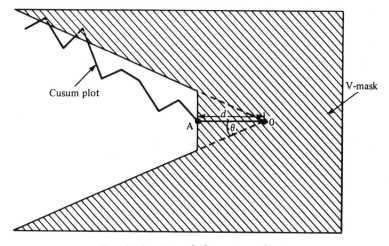

Fig. 11.8   V-mask for cusum chart

As we shall see later, the methods are theoretically equivalent, but the mechanics are different. These need to be explained.

V-Masks

In 1959 G.A. Barnard described a V-shaped mask which could be superimposed on the cusum plot. This is usually drawn on a transparent overlay and is as shown in Fig. 11.8. The mask is placed over the chart so that the line AO is parallel with the horizontal axis, the vertex O points forwards, and the point A lies on top of the last sample plot. A significant change in the process is indicated by part of the cusum plot being covered by either limb of the V-mask, as in Fig. 11.8. This should be followed by a search for assignable causes. If all the points previously plotted fall within the V shape, the process is assumed to be in a state of statistical control.

The design of the V-mask obviously depends upon the choice of the lead distance d (measured in number of sample plots) and the angle θ. This may be made empirically by drawing a number of masks and testing out each one on past data. Since the original work on V-masks, there have been developed many quantitative methods of design. One of these will be described later.

Decision Intervals

Procedures exist for detecting changes in one direction only. The amount of change in that direction is compared with a predetermined amount – the decision interval h, and corrective action is taken when that value is exceeded. The modern decision interval procedures may be used as one- or two-sided methods. An example will illustrate the basic concepts.

Suppose that we are manufacturing valve pistons, with a target diameter (t) of 10.0 mm and we wish to detect when the process mean diameter decreases – the tolerance is 9.6 mm. Our target value is 10.0 mm and the process standard deviation is 0.1 mm. We set a reference value, k, at a point half-way between the target and the so called Reject Quality Level (RQL), the point beyond which an unacceptable proportion of reject material will be produced. With a normally distributed variable, the RQL may be estimated from the specification tolerance (T) and the process standard deviation (σ). If, for example, it is agreed that no more than one piston in 1000 should be manufactured outside the tolerance, then the RQL will be approximately 3σ inside the specification limit. So for the lower tolerance T:

$$RQL_L = T_L + 3\sigma$$
$$= 9.6 + 0.3 = 9.9 \text{ mm}$$

and the reference value is:

$$k_L = (t + RQL_L)/2$$
$$= (10.0 + 9.9)/2 = 9.95 \text{ mm}$$

For a process having an upper tolerance limit:

$$RQL_U = T_U - 3\sigma$$
$$\text{and } k_U = (RQL_U + t)/2$$

Alternatively, the *RQL* may be set nearer to the tolerance value to allow a higher proportion of defective material. For example, the RQL_L set at $T_L + 2\sigma$ will allow ca. 2.5% of the products to fall below the lower specification limit. For the purposes of this example, we shall set the RQL_L at 9.9 mm and k_L at 9.95 mm.

Cusum values are calculated as before, but subtracting k_L instead of t from the individual results:

$$Sr = \sum_{i=1}^{r} (x_i - k_L)$$

This time the plot of Sr against r will be expected to show a rising trend if the target value is obtained, since the subtraction of k_L will always lead to a positive result. For this reason, the cusum chart is plotted in a different way. As soon as the cusum rises above zero, a new series is started, only negative values and the first positive cusums being used. The chart may have the appearance of Fig. 11.9. When the cusum drops below the decision interval,

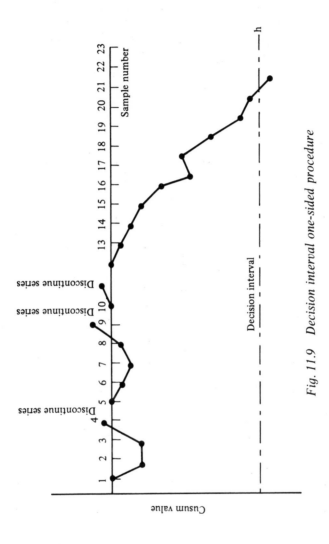

Fig. 11.9   Decision interval one-sided procedure

$-h$, a shift of the process mean to a value below k_L is indicated. This procedure calls attention to those downward shifts in the process average that are considered to be of importance.

The one-sided procedure may, of course, be used to detect shifts in the positive direction by the appropriate selection of k. In this case k will be higher than the target value and the decision to investigate the process will be made when Sr has a positive value which rises above the interval h.

It is possible to run two one-sided schemes concurrently to detect both increases and decreases in results. This requires the use of two reference values k_L and k_U, which are respectively half-way between the target value and the lower and upper tolerance levels, and two decision intervals $-h$ and h. This gives rise to the so-called two-sided decision procedure.

Two-sided Decision Intervals and V-Masks

When two one-sided schemes are run with upper and lower reference values, k_U and k_L, the overall procedure is equivalent to using a V-shaped mask. If the distance between two plots on the horizontal scale is equal to the distance on the vertical scale representing a change of v, then the two-sided decision interval scheme is the same as the V-mask scheme if:

$$k_U - t = t - k_L = v - \tan\theta$$

and
$$h = -h = dv \tan\theta = d|t - k|$$

A demonstration of this equivalence is given by K.W. Kemp in Applied Statistics (1962) vol. 11, page 20.

CHAPTER 12

Quantitative Decision Procedures for Use With Cusum Charts

12.1 Design of Cusum Charts with Decision Rules for Variables

Average Run Length to Detection (ARL)

As we have seen in earlier chapters, a useful measurement of the ability of a control chart to detect a change is the Average Run Length to Detection (ARL). This is the number of points which must be plotted before the control scheme will pick up the change. To design a cusum chart with decision procedure, an ARL is chosen for when the process mean reaches the Reject Quality Level (RQL). We have seen that the RQL may be estimated for variables from knowledge of the specification tolerance and the process standard deviation, σ. The ARL at the RQL is set at a small value, say 2 to 5 to enable a rapid detection of such a change.

We need also to set an ARL at the target value. This is obviously set quite high, since we do not wish to indicate a change when no change has occurred. The ARL at the target, or so-called Acceptable Quality Level (AQL), is typically set at 500. This is equivalent to setting two action lines on Shewart charts at a 1 in 1000 chance of being exceeded if the process remains stable.

Design of Cusum Charts for Variables

The following parameters will be used in the design of decision intervals and V-masks:

$$t = AQL = \text{Target Quality or Acceptable Quality Level}$$
$$RQL_U \text{ or } RQL_L = \text{Reject Quality Level}$$
$$k_U \text{ or } k_L = \text{Reference value}$$
$$n = \text{Sample size}$$
$$\sigma = \text{Process Standard Deviation}$$
$$L = ARL \text{ at } AQL \ (t).$$

$$L_R = ARL \text{ at } RQL$$

$$h \text{ or } -h = \text{Decision Interval}$$

In the design of V-masks and decision intervals for variables it will be assumed that the variable is Normally distributed.

A cusum chart may be designed to give approximately the required *ARLs* at the *AQL* and *RQL*. To do this usually requires the use of a computer to solve the mathematical equations that arise in the formulation of the problem. The manual method presented here involves the use of a nomogram, constructed by K.W. Kemp 'Applied Statistics' (1962) II p. 23, which summarizes the results of this computation. The nomogram of Fig. 12.1 may be used to design a V-mask or a decision interval scheme from knowledge of σ and specified *AQL* and *RQL*, with desired run lengths L_A and L_R. The sample size may be specified or not fixed.

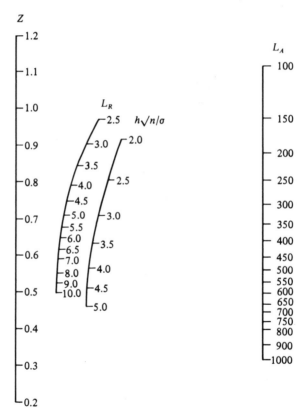

Fig. 12.1   *Nomogram for calculation of cusum decision procedures*

Decision Interval

To illustrate the method, we shall design a one-sided scheme for valve pistons with the following data:

$$AQL = 10.0\,\text{mm}$$
$$L_A = 500$$
$$RQL = 9.9\,\text{mm}$$
$$L_R = 5 \text{ or less}$$
$$\sigma = 0.1\,\text{mm}$$

Firstly we must calculate the reference value:

$$k_L = (AQL + RQL)/2$$
$$= (10.0 + 9.9)/2 = 9.95\,\text{mm}$$

Now we must find the value of h which will provide the desired average run lengths L_A and L_R. From here the procedure depends upon whether the sample size n is fixed or the chart design is to include sample size.

Sample Size Fixed – say $n = 5$
(1) Calculate:

$$Z = |k_L - AQL|\sqrt{n}/\sigma$$
$$= |9.95 - 10.0|\sqrt{5}/0.1 = 1.118$$

(2) Place a straight edge onto Fig. 12.1 so that the point 500 on the L_A scale is connected to the value 1.118 on the left-hand scale for Z.
(3) Note where the straight edge intersects the L_R curve and check that this is below the required *ARL* value. In our example, this is 2.73 which meets the stipulated 5 or less. If the L_R from the nomogram is higher than the maximum required, the sample size must be increased to raise the value of $|k - AQL|\sqrt{n}/\sigma$ and hence L_R. In these circumstances, the procedure for sample size not fixed should be followed.
(4) With the straight edge still in the same place, read off the value of $h\sqrt{n}/\sigma$ from the second curved line. For the valve piston diameters, $h\sqrt{n}/\sigma = 2.12$. The decision interval h may now be calculated:

$$h = 2.12\sigma/\sqrt{n} = 2.12 \times 0.1/\sqrt{5} = 0.095\,\text{mm}$$

From this stepwise procedure we have designed a scheme which operates as follows:

● Take random samples of 5 pistons and measure their diameters, x_j
● Calculate the sample means $\bar{x}_i$

- From each sample mean subtract the reference value k_L, 9.95 mm
- Plot the cumulated difference,

$$Sr = \sum_{i=1}^{r} (\bar{x}_i - k)$$

- If the cusum becomes positive, restart the cusum plot
- If the cusum plot drops below a decision interval $-h$ drawn at -0.095 mm, we conclude that the process mean is out of control.

Sample Size Not Fixed – n is unknown
1. Place a straight edge onto Fig. 12.1 so that the value 500 on the right hand L_A scale is connected to the point 5 on the curved L_R line.
2. Record the value where the straight edge intersects the left hand Z scale. In the case of the piston diameters, $Z = 0.742$.
3. Calculate n from

$$Z = |k - AQL|\sqrt{n}/\sigma$$
$$\sqrt{n} = Z\sigma/|k - AQL| = 0.742 \times 0.1/9.95 - 10.0 = 1.484$$
$$\therefore n = 2.2 \quad \text{or} \quad \underline{3} \text{ to the next integer.}$$

4. Calculate a new value of Z, using the integer value of n, i.e. 3:

$$Z = |9.95 - 10.0|\sqrt{3}/0.1 = 0.866$$

5. Place a straight edge onto Fig. 12.1 connecting this new value of Z to the point 500 on the L_A scale.
6. Read off the value where the straight edge intersects the $h\sqrt{n}/\sigma$ curve. In our example this occurs at $h\sqrt{n}/\sigma = 2.73$, and the decision interval may be calculated:

$$h = 2.73\sigma/\sqrt{n} = 2.73 \times 0.1/\sqrt{3} = 0.158 \text{ mm}$$

The straight edge also intersects the L_R line at the point 3.95, which is below the desired ARL of 5 at the RQL of 9.9 mm.

The scheme designed in this way operates exactly the same as the scheme for fixed sample size, but with different values of $n (= 3)$ and $h (= -0.158$ mm$)$.

V-Mask

We may design a V-mask for use in the example above, when the AQL or target value is subtracted from each sample mean and the whole cusum chart plotted.

$$t = AQL = 10.00 \text{ mm}$$
$$L_A = 500$$

$$RQL = 9.9 \, \text{mm}$$
$$L_R = 5 \text{ or less}$$
$$n = 5$$
$$\sigma = 0.1 \, \text{mm}$$
$$k_L = 9.95$$
$$h = 0.095$$

Assuming that we try to set the distance on the horizontal scale between two sample plots equal to the distance representing approximately $2\sigma_{\bar{x}}$ on the vertical scale. First we must calculate $2\sigma_{\bar{x}}$:

$$2\sigma_{\bar{x}} = 2\sigma/\sqrt{n} = 2 \times 0.1\sqrt{5} = 0.0894 \, \text{mm}$$

If one sample is plotted every 1 cm on the horizontal scale, the sensible vertical scale has 1 cm of the graph paper equivalent to 0.1 mm cusum plot. Thus, the value of v, the ratio of a sample plot distance on the horizontal scale to the unit distance on the vertical scale is 0.1.

The relevant equations may now be used to calculate θ and d:

$$t - k = v \tan \theta$$
$$0.05 = 0.1 \tan \theta$$
$$\tan \theta = 0.5$$
$$\theta = 26° \, 36'$$
$$h = dv \tan \theta = d|t - k|$$
$$0.095 = d \times 0.1 \times 0.5 = 0.05d$$
$$d = 1.9 \text{ sample plots}$$

12.2 Decision Procedures for Attribute Data

As we saw at the beginning of Chapter 11, cusum charts may be plotted for attribute data. Decision intervals and certain types of V-masks may also be used. The schemes described here are for number defective/of defects cusum charts, which have wide application. The parameters for an inspection scheme and cusum chart for attributes may be found from Table 12.1. The values in this table, calculated by Kemp 'Applied Statistics' (1962) II, p. 29, have been chosen to give schemes requiring the smallest sample sizes at an average run length at the AQL (L_A) of 500. The Poisson distribution has been used, as an approximation of the Binomial, to obtain these values. To use the table, we must know or set the proportions defective at the AQL (p_1)

Table 12.1   Values of np, k, and h for proportion defective
cusum charts from R and L, when La = 500

L	R	2.5	3.0	3.5	4.0
	np	1.18	0.66	0.54	0.38
5.0	k	2.00	1.20	1.20	0.90
	h	5.00	4.00	3.00	2.75
	np	0.64	0.46	0.35	0.24
7.5	k	1.20	0.90	0.80	0.60
	h	3.75	3.50	3.00	2.75
	np	0.50	0.32	0.24	0.16
10.0	k	0.90	0.70	0.60	0.40
	h	3.75	3.00	2.75	2.50

and the *RQL* (p_2). *R* is then the ratio of these values:

$$R = p_2/p_1$$

Entering the table with the calculated value of *R* and the required *ARL* at
the *RQL* (L_R), we may find *n* (sample size), *k* (reference value), and *h* (decision
interval). *n* is, of course, obtained by dividing by p_1 the value of np_1 from the
table. An example should clarify the use of this simple method.

A furniture manufacturer wishes to design a cusum chart with decision
interval for use in the process inspection of tables. The average proportion
defective being produced is 1% and this is regarded as the *AQL* ($p_1 = 0.01$).
The level of defectives at which rejection is required is 4% ($p_2 = 0.04$). The
producer would like to detect a change to the *RQL* after 5 sample plots
($L_R = 5$). $R = p_2/p_1 = 4$ and from Table 12.1 we find $np_1 = 0.38$, $k = 0.9$,
$h = 2.75$. We may now calculate the sample size:

$$n = np_1/p_1 = 0.38/0.1 = 38$$

Hence, the furniture manufacturer should select at random a sample of 38
tables, examine them and count the number of defectives in the sample (*x*),
subtract 0.90 (*k*) from this figure, and start to plot the results when defectives
are found in the sample. If the cusum falls below zero a new series is begun.
When the cusum of $\Sigma(x - k)$ exceeds the decision interval (*h*) of 2.75, the
process is investigated for assignable causes.

A V-mask may be used as an alternative to the decision interval method.
Here, of course, the average number of defectives, np_1, is subtracted from
each sample value and the whole cusum chart plotted. The method may be
used only to detect an increase in *p* by designing a half-V-mask with only
one limb. This is because of the skewness of the Poisson distribution at
small values of np_1. The angle θ for the lower limit of a V-mask and the lead

distance, d may be designed for the furniture example:

$$\tan \theta = |k - np_1|/v$$

$$= 0.9 - 0.38/v$$

If $v = 1$, i.e. one sample plot every 1 cm on the horizontal scale, and 1 cm on the vertical axis represents a cusum plot of 1:

$$\tan \theta = 0.52$$

$$\theta = 27°30'$$

$$d = h/v \tan \theta$$

$$= 2.75/0.52$$

$$= 5.29 \text{ sample plots}$$

This method may also be used to design a scheme for a fixed sample size by finding the value of np_1 in Table 12.1 which is nearest to the calculated quantity.

12.3   Cusum Charts in Use

One of the major criteria in the assessment of any process control scheme is its efficiency in detecting change in the process average, whether this be a measurable quantity or an attribute parameter. This is usually measured by the expected number of samples which need to be taken before the change is detected – the average run length (ARL).

To carry out a meaningful comparison between two schemes, it is necessary to make the ARLs the same when the process is running at the acceptable quality level. In all the cusum cases we have examined in this chapter, this $ARL(L_A)$ has been set at 500.

Variables – Mean Chart v. Cusum Chart

Detection by mean chart of a shift in process average is by a point plotting outside the action line. This is usually set at a probability of 0.001 or one-in-a-thousand chance of being crossed if the process average remains at the AQL. The $ARL (L_A)$ is the reciprocal of this probability: $1/0.001 = 1000$. To make a comparison with cusum charts, however, we must convert the ARL for the mean chart to $L_A = 500$. From the Normal tables (Appendix A) we can see that this may be achieved by setting the limits for detection at $\bar{X} \pm 2.88\sigma_{\bar{x}}$ instead of the usual $\bar{X} \pm 3.09\sigma_{\bar{x}}$.

Using an example from the filling of shampoo bottles, we may draw up a comparison table of ARLs for various increases in process mean, for the mean and cusum charts when:

$$\text{Target process mean } (AQL) \quad = 50\,\text{ml}$$
$$\text{Process Standard Deviation } (\sigma) = 0.25\,\text{ml}$$
$$\text{Sample Size } (n) \qquad\qquad\quad = 4$$
$$\text{ARL at AQL } (L_A) \qquad\qquad = 500$$

and we wish to detect a change in the process average to 50.2 ml.

Mean Chart (Shewhart)

For the one-sided test of increase in mean:

$$\text{Upper Action Limit} = \bar{X} + 2.88\,\sigma/\sqrt{n}$$
$$= 50 + (2.88 \times 0.25/\sqrt{4})$$
$$= 50.36\,\text{ml}$$

For a change in process mean of 0.2 ml the *ARL* to detection may be calculated:

$$\sigma_{\bar{x}} = \sigma/\sqrt{n} = 0.25/\sqrt{4} = 0.125\,\text{ml}$$

Therefore, a change of 0.2 ml = change of $+\,1.6\,\sigma_{\bar{x}}$. The distance U, between the new mean and the upper action line is:

$$U = 2.88\,\sigma_{\bar{x}} - 1.6\,\sigma_{\bar{x}} = 1.28\,\sigma_{\bar{x}}$$

From U and the Normal tables (Appendix A) we find that the probability of a sample mean falling outside the upper action line is 0.1003. The *ARL* to detection at the new mean is 1/0.1003, i.e. ca. 10.

Cusum Chart

The relevant information for the design of a cusum chart with decision interval is as follows:

$$t = AQL = 50\,\text{ml} \qquad L_A = 500$$
$$RQL_U = 50.2\,\text{ml}$$
$$n = 4 \qquad\qquad\qquad \sigma = 0.25\,\text{ml}$$

The reference value, k_U is determined as follows:

$$k_U = (QRL_U + AQL)/2 = 50.1\,\text{ml}$$

Now,

$$Z = |k_U - AQL|\sqrt{n}/\sigma$$
$$= |50.1 - 50.0|\sqrt{4}/0.2 = 0.8$$

Using Fig. 12.1, a straight edge is set to connect 500 on the L_A scale to the value 0.8 on the Z scale. This intersects the curves at 4.47 for L_R and 2.94 for $h\sqrt{n}/\sigma$. From the latter, the decision interval h may be calculated:

$$h = 2.94\,\sigma/\sqrt{n} = 2.94 \times 0.25/\sqrt{4} = 0.37\,\text{ml}$$

and the *ARL* to detection of a change in process mean from 50.0 ml to 50.2 ml is approximately 3.

The two schemes may be compared in the average number of samples which need to be taken to detect the change in process mean. A relative detection efficiency index (*RE*) enables the comparison to be quantified:

$$RE = \text{Relative detection efficiency index of}$$
$$\text{scheme 1 v. scheme 2}$$

$$RE = \frac{ARL \text{ to detection of scheme 2}}{ARL \text{ to detection of scheme 1}} \times 100\%$$

In the above example the relative efficiency of the Shewhart mean chart versus the cusum with decision interval scheme is:

$$RE = \tfrac{3}{10} \times 100\% = 30\%$$

It will be found that a cusum chart with decision interval or V-mask is always superior to a Shewhart control scheme. The systems are comparable at very small or very large changes in process mean, but for changes of the order 0.25σ to 1σ, the cusum chart can be four times more efficient at detecting changes than the Shewhart chart.

Cusum or Shewhart Chart?

Attribute schemes behave in a very similar manner to those for variables. Comparisons by relative detection efficiency can be made using Table 12.1, and again the cusum control system will be found to be up to four times quicker in detecting a change in the average number of defectives or defects. As with variable schemes, the relative efficiency depends on the magnitude of the change.

The cusum control systems with decision intervals and V-masks are clearly more efficient than the Shewhart charts in detecting changes in process average. There are, however, other factors to be considered in the selection of an appropriate control scheme. For example, Shewhart charts are invariably simpler to design and plot than cusum charts. Even more important, the former are far easier to interpret than the latter and it is this factor which often favours the choice of Shewhart charts in direct production applications.

The cusum chart, on the other hand, usually finds acceptability in the hands of supervisory or management personnel. This arbitrary distinction is, of course, very dependent on the individual company and its workforce, and it is possible to provide the correct form of training which will overcome any difficulties. It is the extreme sensitivity of the cusum chart which may mislead, and random fluctuations in the parameter under study will lead to apparent changes if only casual visual inspection of the chart is used. Wherever possible, the significance of any change should be examined using a V-mask or decision interval scheme. If care is exercised the cusum chart offers a powerful diagnostic tool for management.

To conclude then, standard Shewhart control charts should be used for process control when simplicity is required and when tests/ inspections/measurements are inexpensive. Improvements in detection efficiency may then be considered to be of secondary importance unless substantial costs will be incurred as a result of producing defective material. Cusum charts may be more appropriate when inspection costs are relatively high, simplicity in use is not vital, and when rapid detection of change is required. As we observed at the beginning of Chapter 11, the use of cusum charts enables fairly accurate estimation of the point at which changes occurred.

CHAPTER 13

Economic Design of Control Charts

13.1 Introduction

In recent years considerable attention has been given to the design of control charts on economic grounds. For a control chart to be used the following parameters must be specified:

sample size, n,

sampling frequency, h (the interval of time between samples),

control limits (set at $k\sigma_{\bar{x}}$ from the Grand Mean).

The selection of these values is effectively the design of the control chart, and traditionally charts have been designed considering only statistical concepts.

The selection of the sample size has been given some attention in Chapter 5 (section 4), but the frequency of sampling is not usually calculated using analytical methods. Typically, the sampling interval is chosen using qualitative guidelines, and is often found to be ca. one hour. The control limits are usually set at $1.96\sigma_{\bar{x}}$ and $3.09\sigma_{\bar{x}}$ from $\bar{X}$ in Britain and $3\sigma_{\bar{x}}$ in the USA.

The design of control charts, however, has economic consequences since the costs of:

- taking samples,
- inspection,
- taking repeat samples and inspection after 'warning' indications,
- investigating 'action' signals and any accompanying loss of production,
- correcting assignable causes,
- defective products reaching the customer,

are all affected by the selection of the control chart parameters. It is logical, therefore, to consider the design of control charts from an economic perspective. The work carried out in this field has involved many mathematical manipulations which are outside the scope of this book.

Several references to the original work have been given at the end of this chapter for the reader who wishes to become familiar with the theoretical background. This chapter will deal only with the practical implications of the simple models which have been conceived. The qualitative aspects of this work should be borne in mind, whether or not the methods are used as described.

13.2   Assumptions and Costs

For an economic model to be formulated for the design of a control chart, certain assumptions about the behaviour of the production process are required. Most of the models suggested make standard assumptions which are summarized below:

1. The production process has one in-control state. For example, if the weights of tablets are being measured, then the in-control state will be associated with the process average weight, when there are no assignable causes operating.

2. There may be several out-of-control states, each one corresponding to a particular assignable cause of variation.

3. The process is assumed to start in-control.

4. The transitions between states are assumed to be 'instantaneous'. Little attention has been given to situations in which processes drift slowly from the in-control to out-of-control states, such as is found with tool wear.

5. A critical assumption, concerned with the nature of movement of the process from an in-control state to an out-of-control condition, is that assignable causes occur at time intervals predicted by a Poisson distribution (see Chapter 10). This is analogous to trying to predict when runs will be scored during a cricket or baseball match. The use of a Poisson process assumes that assignable causes occur on average λ per unit time. Hence, the process will remain in-control on average $1/\lambda$ units of time, with $1/\lambda$ changing exponentially. The nature of these process shifts is sometimes called the process failure mechanism.

6. The process is not self-correcting, that is once an out-of-control state has been reached, the process can only be brought back in-control by action following the appropriate signal from the control chart. Some models allow transitions between different out-of-control states, but these always assume that such movements involve further deterioration of quality.

7. A search will be undertaken to detect an assignable cause whenever an action signal is obtained from the control chart.

8. The process will be allowed to continue in operation during the search for an assignable cause. Production will not cease whilst the search is in progress.

9. The cost of adjustment to eliminate an assignable cause will not be charged to the control chart programme.

Costs

The costs of operating a process control system are obviously an important element in the economic design of control charts. Three areas of cost are usually considered:

1. Sampling, inspection, and testing.
2. Investigation of an action signal, including the correction of any assignable cause found.
3. Production of defective material.

The costs associated with sampling, inspection, and test consist of fixed and variable components, cf and cv respectively. So these costs for a sample size n are:

$$cf + ncv$$

The fixed costs will be comprised of the expenditure on measuring equipment, including calibration, materials, the employment of suitable staff and the provision of suitable accommodation and administrative support. The variable costs are incurred only as each sample is taken and include the costs of plotting control charts.

The investigation and correction, if required, of possible assignable causes have been the subject of much work and several models have been formulated. Some workers prefer to treat the costs of correcting assignable causes differently from those associated with investigating false alarms, and have suggested different cost coefficients for each. Linked to this is the assumption that the costs of correcting the process will depend upon the type of assignable cause present. Other authors have simplified this particular cost aspect by using only one coefficient for the average cost of investigating and possibly correcting the process from which an action signal has been obtained. This is based on the assumption that large shifts are easy to find but difficult to correct, and conversely small shifts are difficult to find but easy to correct.

The production of defective output brings the costs of sorting, scrap, rework, dealing with customer complaints, replacements under warranty, etc. A more serious but very difficult cost to ascertain is that associated with loss of goodwill, following the sale of defective products. Designers of economic models have found great difficulty with this aspect and it is in this area that most of the systems offered are weak. Probably the most satisfactory models suggest either a single average cost coefficient, which is assumed to be incurred on a per item / per unit time basis, or a coefficient for the total loss in profit when the process is running out-of-control.

It is helpful to summarize the costs indentified so far and represent them in a form which will be used in the simplified models recommended:

cf – the fixed costs of sampling and inspecting/testing/measuring.

cv – the variable cost of sampling, measuring, calculating and plotting each sample value on the control charts.

I – the cost of investigating an action signal whether or not assignable causes exists.

C – the cost of correcting an assignable cause.

L – the total loss in profit when the process is running out of control.

13.3   Economic Design of Mean Charts

The early work in this field was carried out by Duncan, and a considerable amount of research has been devoted to the design of mean charts on economic grounds. Models exist for single and multiple assignable causes and it is not proposed to examine all the developments here. Montgomery has written a well referenced review of the literature in this field and the interested reader will find this worthy of further study. It is proposed here to present the general conclusions of the mathematical solutions, and the simplest of practical, semi-economic models.

Let us assume, as we did in Chapter 5, that the shift in process mean which we wish to detect is expressed as a multiple of the process standard deviation – say δ, and that the interval between samples is h hours. The following general conclusions arise out of the various numerical solutions to the relevant equations:

1. The magnitude of the shift in mean which we wish to detect, δ, largely determines the optimum sample size. For fairly large shifts of two or more standard deviations ($\delta \geqslant 2$), small sample sizes of $n = 2$ to 8 will usually be optimum. When the shift in mean is smaller – say $\delta = 1$ to 2, then larger optimum sample sizes of $n = 10$ to 20 may be required. Very small shifts of $\delta \leqslant 0.5$ may require samples of size $n = 40$ or more.

2. The total loss in profit when the process is running out-of-control, L has the largest effect on the choice of sampling frequency. The larger the

value of L, the smaller the interval between samples, h. Less frequent sampling will be required when lower penalties for out-of-control production are incurred.

3. The setting of the control limits, and to a lesser extent the sample size, are affected by the costs associated with investigating an action signal, I. If I is large, wider control limits should be set and a larger sample size used. This reduces the incidence of false alarms as the costs of searching for assignable causes increase.

4. All three control chart design parameters: n, h, and k are affected by the costs of sampling. An increase in the fixed cost of sampling, cf causes an increase in h, the interval between samples, and usually slightly larger sample sizes. For high variable costs of sampling, cv, values of n and k are usually low, that is narrow control limits and small, relatively infrequent samples.

5. The interval between samples, h is affected by changes in the average number of assignable causes occurring per hour, λ. High values of λ result in a greater sampling frequency.

6. Errors in estimating cost coefficients do not have a great effect on the optimum economic design of the control charts. This is good news since the identification of costs is the most difficult aspect of using these techniques. The optimum design is, however, relatively sensitive to errors in estimates of the magnitude of the shift (δ), the process mean when in control (μ), and the process standard deviation (σ).

7. Values of n, k, and h, selected arbitrarily, have been compared with the optimum economic design for several simulated process conditions and found to result in large economic penalties.

13.4   Economic Design of Other Control Charts

The development of economic models for the design of control charts has concentrated on mean charts. However, the general approach has been extended to other types of charts. This section will briefly summarize the work on fraction defective and cumulative sum control charts, and make some comments about the usage of economic models.

The economic design of fraction defective control charts has been studied extensively and several authors have investigated single assignable cause economic models. The total costs of sampling, searching for assignable causes, process adjustment, and production of unacceptable material over a fixed time period have been formulated. This period is assumed to start and end with a scheduled process 'set-up' or adjustment that places the process in the in-control state. The general conclusions from these models may be summarized as follows:

1. Small process shifts are typically accompanied by larger sample sizes and longer sampling intervals than is optimal for cases in which the shift is large. There is little support for widespread use of arbitrary sample sizes, such as $n = 50$.

2. Changes in cost coefficients produce expected changes in the optimal control chart design. For example, increasing inspection costs reduce the sample size and increase the sampling interval.

3. The more frequently the assignable cause occurs, the shorter the optimal sampling interval, although in general each sample should be smaller. The impact of a more frequently occurring shift is to increase the overall sampling effort.

The economic design of cusum charts for controlling the mean of a normally distributed variable with a known standard deviation has been studied. The charts are maintained to detect a single assignable cause of variation, which takes the form of a shift of known magnitude. The assumptions include that the process is shut down while a search for trouble is made. If the signal is not a false alarm, time is taken to correct as well as find the offending cause. An approximate expected cost function is formulated based on the assumption that the occurrence of an assignable cause occurs halfway between samples. The model expresses the expected cost per unit of time as a function of the sample size n, decision interval h, and the V-mask design parameters d and θ. In subsequent development of the early models, it was found that sampling costs tend to affect the sampling frequency primarily, with increases in both fixed and variable costs of sampling resulting in less frequent samples being economically favourable. The cusum chart is not quite as sensitive to errors in specifying the magnitude of the shift in process mean as is the Shewhart mean chart.

Control charts based on moving averages are very effective for detecting small shifts, as we have seen in Chapter 7. However, little economic analysis of this type of control chart has been conducted.

The author has found generally that very few practitioners have implemented economic models for the design of control charts. This is somewhat surprising since most practitioners claim that a major objective in the use of statistical process control procedures is to reduce costs. There are a number of possible reasons for the lack of practical implementation of this methodology:

1. The mathematical models and their associated optimization schemes are relatively complex and are often presented in a manner that is difficult

for the practitioners to understand and use. The availability of computer programs for these models and the development of simplified approximate optimization procedures suitable for manual computation may help to alleviate this problem.

2. There is difficulty in estimating costs and other model parameters. Fortunately, costs do not have to be estimated with high precision, although other model components, such as the magnitude of the shift, require relatively accurate determination.

3. Most of the attention has been focussed on mean charts. The task of formulating economic models for other charts such as range or c-charts is yet to be accomplished.

4. Most models assume that the assignable cause takes the form of a shift in the process of known magnitude. In practice, there may be cases where the process level changes are of a continuous type, or that the process may have more than one out-of-control state.

5. Many unrealistic assumptions are made in order to justify the formulation of a model. Accordingly, some of the models are complex and may not be useful for practical applications.

6. Many control techniques have been proposed and it is difficult for the practitioner to select the most appropriate procedure for a given situation.

As a guide to the implementation of economic models, the cost or value of the products should be evaluated and initial efforts in economic modelling should be concentrated on those products (or processes) of greatest value. Using the Pareto principle which we met in Chapter 3, we frequently find that a relatively small proportion of the products manufactured accounts for most of the cost of production or of sales revenue. In stock control, the 'ABC system' defines these as 'A items', while 'B items' and 'C items' are more numerous, but account for proportionately less value to the organization. The more sophisticated stock control techniques are concentrated on the A items. Similarly, it is not at all necessary to control every process using an economically designed system. The use of this type of modelling should be confined initially to those products carrying the greatest costs or value.

Selected References (alphabetical order)

1. Chiu, W.K. 'The economic design of cusum charts for controlling normal means', *Applied Statistics*, Vol. 23, No. 3, pp 420–433, 1974.

2. Chiu, W.K. 'Economic design of attribute control charts', *Technometrics*, Vol. 17, No. 1, pp 81–87, 1975.

3. Chiu, W.K. and Wetherill, G.B. 'A simplified scheme for the economic design of x̄-charts', *Journal of Quality Technology*, Vol. **6**, No. 2, pp 66–69, 1974.

4. Duncan, A.J. 'The economic design of x̄-charts used to maintain current control of a process', *Journal of the American Statistical Association*, Vol. **51**, No. 274, pp 228–242, 1956.

5. Gibra, I.N. 'Recent developments in control chart techniques', *Journal of Quality Technology*, Vol. **7**, No. 4, pp 183–192, 1975.

6. Montgomery, D.C. 'The economic design of control charts; a review and literature survey', *Journal of Quality Technology*, Vol. **12**, No. 2, pp 78–87, 1980.

CHAPTER 14

The Implementation of Statistical Process Control (SPC)

14.1 Introduction

The author and his colleagues have carried out structured investigations into the usage of statistical methods of process quality control in manufacturing industry. The various techniques of statistical quality control (SQC) have been available to industry for over sixty years. Shewhart's first book on control charts was written in 1924. There is now a vast academic literature on the subject and most production management textbooks discuss some of the techniques in detail. However, the research work at the University of Bradford Management Centre has shown that extensive use is not made of SQC.

Where SQC is in use it has been shown that quality related costs are usually known and low, and that often the use of SQC was specified by a customer, at least initially. This is particularly true in the case of statistical process control (SPC) where companies using the techniques frequently require their suppliers to use them also. Companies using SQC/SPC find it to be of considerable benefit and the techniques tend to remain in use from their introduction.

The major reason found for the low usage of SPC is lack of knowledge, particularly amongst senior managers. Although they sometimes recognize quality as being an important part of corporate strategy, they do not appear to know what effective steps to take in order to carry out the strategy. Too often quality is seen as an abstract property and not as a measurable and controllable parameter.

It would appear that, as a large majority of companies who have tried SPC are happy with its performance and continue to use it, the point at which resistance occurs is in introducing the techniques. Clearly there is a need to increase knowledge, awareness of the benefits, and an understanding of how SPC should be introduced.

14.2 Successful Users of SPC and the Benefits Derived

In-depth work in companies which use SPC successfully has given clear evidence that customer quality assurance schemes push manufacturers towards the use of process capability assessments and process control charts. It must be recognized, however, that this external pressure does not necessarily lead to an understanding of either the value or the relevance of the techniques.

Close examination of companies which use SPC incorrectly showed that there was no real commitment or encouragement from senior management. It was apparent in some of these firms that lack of knowledge and even positive deceit can lead to unjustifiable claims to either customers or management. No system of quality control will survive the lack of full commitment by senior management to the achievement of quality. The failure to understand or accept this will lead to loss of control of quality and the very high costs associated with it.

Truly successful users of SPC can only remain so when the senior management is both aware of and committed to the continued use and development of the techniques. The most commonly occurring influence contributing to the use of SPC was exerted by an enthusiastic member of the management team. Typically this person works within either the production or quality function and co-ordinates all activities associated with SPC.

Other themes which recur in successful user companies are:

● One problem should be tackled at a time and dealt with thoroughly before moving on to others.
● All the people involved in the use of the techniques should understand what they are being asked to do and why it should help them.
● Training, followed by clear and written instructions on the agreed procedures, must be structured.

These requirements are, of course, contained within the general principles of good quality management systems.

The benefits which are derived from the application of statistical methods at the process control stage are many and varied. A major spin-off is the improved or continuing reputation for high quality products. This leads to a steady or expanding, always healthy, share of the market. The improved process and product conformity derived causes a direct reduction in external failure costs – warranty claims, customer complaints, and the intractable 'loss of good will'. The corresponding reduction in costs of internal failure – scrap, rework, secondary or low value product, etc. generates a bonus increase in productivity, by reducing the size of the 'hidden plant' which is devoted to producing non-conforming products.

The greater degree of process control allows an overall reduction in inspection and test effort, often resulting in a reduction or redeployment of direct inspection staff levels. The benefits are not confined to substantial lowering of total quality related costs, for additional information, such as vendor rating, allows more efficient management of non-production areas such as purchasing, design, and even marketing.

Two major requirements then appear to be necessary for the successful implementation of SPC, and are present in all companies which continue to use the techniques successfully and derive the benefits:

1. A real commitment from senior management.
2. A dedicated and well informed quality-related manager.

It has also been noted by the author and his colleagues that the intervention of a 'third party' such as a consultant or external trainer has a very positive effect.

14.3   The Implementation of SPC

The lack of knowledge and understanding of SPC derives largely from the fact that, in general, technical and management education does not include a practical approach to the introduction of quality control techniques. Successful implementation of SPC depends on the approach to the work being structured. This applies to all companies, whatever their size, technology, or product range. Unsuccessful SPC implementation programmes usually show weaknesses within either the structure of the project or commitment to it. Any procedure adopted requires commitment from senior management to the objectives of the work and an in-house coordinator being made available. The selection of a specific project to launch the introduction of SPC should take account of the knowledge available and the control of the process being:

● highly desirable,
● possible within a reasonable time period, and
● possible by the use of techniques requiring, at most, simple training for their introduction.

Many companies are simply not aware of the capabilities of their manufacturing processes. Consequently control of them is nebulous.

The first barrier which usually has to be overcome is that manufacturing companies pay insufficient attention to training, outside the technological requirements of their processes. With a few notable exceptions, they are often unsympathetic to the devotion of anything beyond minimal effort and time for training in the wider techniques of management and control. This exacerbates the basic lack of knowledge of process control and derives from lack of real support from the senior management. Lame excuses such as 'the operators will never understand it', 'it seems like a lot of extra work', or 'we lack the necessary facilities' must not be tolerated. A further frequently occurring source of difficulty, related to knowledge and training, is the absence from the management team of a knowledgeable enthusiast.

The impact of the intervention of a third party is remarkable. The third party's views will be seldom different from those of some of the management but are simply more willingly received. The expertise of the 'consultant', whilst indispensable, may well be incidental to the wider impact of their presence.

Proposed Methodology for Implementation

The conclusions of the author's work in helping companies to implement SPC programmes is perhaps best summarized by detailing a proposed methodology for introducing SPC into a manufacturing company. This is given below under the various headings which categorize the essential steps in the process:

1. Formalize the Procedures

The 'quality status' of the company has no bearing on the possibility of help being of value – the company may or may not have quality problems, in any event it will always benefit from a review of its quality systems. The first formal step should be a written outline of the objectives, programme of work, timing, and reporting mechanism. Within this formal approach it is necessary to ensure that the company's quality policy is defined in writing, that the requirement for quality documentation including a quality manual is recognized, that a management representative responsible for quality is appointed. His role should be clearly defined, together with any part to be played by a third party. A useful method of formalizing reporting is to prepare on a regular basis, a Memorandum Account of Quality Related Costs – this monitors progress and acts as a useful focus for management.

2. Check the Specification

Does a specification exist and is it reasonable? It is not possible to manufacture a product or carry out the manufacturing operations without a specification – yet written specifications are often absent, out of date, or totally unachievable. The specification should describe in adequate detail what has to be done, how it has to be done, and how inspection or test will show that it has been done. It will also indicate who is responsible for the manufacture and test as well as what records shall be kept and the prescribed action when the specification is not met.

3. Emphasize the Need for Process Quality Control

For a variety of reasons the control of quality is still frequently perceived as being closely related to inspection, inspectors, traceability, and heavy administrative costs. It is vital that the company recognizes that the way to control product quality (both the company's products and those of its suppliers) is to control the various manufacturing processes within the company. The inspection of final product can serve as a method of measuring the effectiveness of the control of the processes, but at final product inspection it is too late to exercise control of the processes. Sorting the good from the bad, which is often attempted at final inspection, is a clear admission of the fact that the company does not expect to be able to control its manufacturing processes.

Process control methods are based on the examination of finished and semi-finished product at an early stage with a view to rapid and effective feedback. Rapid feedback gives tighter control, saves adding value to defective items, saves time, and reduces the impact of defective material on scheduling and hence output. Effective feedback can only be achieved by the use of statistically based process quality control methods – other methods will ignore the difference between random and non-random events and consequential action will lead to 'hunting' the process.

Where the quality status of a company is particularly low and no reliable records are available, it may prove necessary to start the work by data collection from either bought-in goods or company products. This search for data is, of course, only a preliminary to process control. In some companies, with very low quality status, it may be necessary to start work on bought-in goods exclusively so as to later turn the finger inwards.

In the majority of cases the problems can only be solved by the adoption of better process control techniques. These techniques are the subject of renewed emphasis in Japan, the USA, and various European countries, including the U.K. New terms are sometimes invented to convey the impression that the techniques are new – the term Statistical Process Control is particularly fashionable now but in fact the techniques have been available to manufacturing industry for decades.

4. Plan for Quality Training

This is always required whether it is to launch a new quality system or to maintain or improve an existing one. Too often companies see training as useful and profitable only when it is limited to the technical processes handled by the company, its suppliers, and its customers. Lack of knowledge of the techniques of quality control is widespread. Training must start at the top of the organization. The amount of time spent need not be large, for example, with proper preparation and qualified teachers, a twenty-hour training programme can:

- provide a good introduction for senior managers – enough to enable them to initiate and follow work within their own organization
- provide a good introduction for middle managers – enough to enable them to follow and encourage work within their organizations
- put quality managers on the right roads – give them the incentive to further their studies either by supervised or unsupervised study
- train inspectors, foremen, supervisors, quality circle facilitators, members or leaders, process and other operators, and provide them with an adequate understanding of the techniques so they may use them without a sense of mystique.

5.   *Follow-up*

For the continued successful use of SPC, the training must be followed-up during the introductory period. Follow-up can take many forms. Ideally, an in-house expert will provide the lead through the design of implementation programmes.

The most satisfactory strategy is to start small and build up a bank of knowledge and experience. Each technique should be introduced alongside existing methods of quality control, if they exist. This allows comparisons to be made between the new and old methods. When confidence has been built up from these comparisons, the SPC techniques will almost take over the control of the processes themselves. Improvements in one or two areas of the company's operations, using this approach, will quickly establish the techniques as reliable methods of controlling quality.

The author and his colleagues have found that another successful formula is the in-company training course plus follow-up workshops. Typically, a 3-day course in SPC is followed within six weeks by a one- or two-day workshop. At this, delegates on the initial training course present the results of their efforts to introduce and use the techniques. Specific process control and implementation problems may be discussed. A series of such workshops will add continuity to the follow-up. Wider company presence should be encouraged in the follow-up activities.

6. *Tackle One Problem at a Time*

In many companies there will be a number of quality problems all requiring attention. The first application of SPC may well be the use of Pareto analysis in order to decide the order in which to tackle the problems. It is then important to choose one problem and work on it until satisfactory progress has been achieved before passing onto a second problem. The way to tackle more than one problem at a time is to engage the interest and commitment of more than one person, but only provided that all such persons are competent to tackle their own selected problem. The co-ordination of these activities then becomes an important task.

7. Record All Observed Data in Detail

A very common fault in manufacturing industry is the failure to record observations properly. This often means that effective analysis of performance is not possible and for subsequent failures, either internal or external, the search for corrective action is frustrated.

The inspector's tick is a frequent feature of many control systems. This actually means that the inspector passed by the machine; it is often assumed to mean that the predetermined observations were carried out and that, although the details are now lost, all was well. Detailed data can be used for performance and trend analysis. Recording detail is also a way of improving the accuracy of records – it is easier to tick-off and accept an item just outside limits than it is to deliberately record erroneously a measured parameter.

8. Measure the Capability of the Process

Process capability must be assessed and not assumed. The capability of all manufacturing processes can be measured. This is true both when the results are assessed as attributes and when measured as variables. Once the capability of the process is known, it can be compared with the specification. Such comparison will either show that the process can achieve the required standard or that it cannot. Where the process is adequate the process capability data can be used to set up control charts for future process control and data recording. Where the process is incapable of meeting the specification, the basis is laid for a rational decision concerning the required action – the revision of the specification or revision of the process.

9. Make Use of the Data on the Process

This may be cumulated, provide feedback, or refined in some way. Cusum techniques for the identification of either short or long term trends can give vital information, not only for process control, but also for fault finding and maintenance planning. The feedback of process control or product data enables remedial action to be planned and taken – this will result in steady improvements over time to both process control and product quality. As the quality or conformance to specification improves, the data can be refined. This may require either greater precision in measurement or less frequent intervention for inspection. The refinement of the data must be directed towards the continuing reduction of the cost of producing the products to the required standards of both design and conformance.

A Final Comment

A good, documented quality management system provides a foundation for the successful application of SPC techniques. It is not possible to 'graft' statistical methods onto a poor quality system. Without adequate written procedures for inspection and test, for the use of inspection equipment, and for the recording of data, SPC will lay dormant.

Much of manufacturing industry would benefit from the implementation of statistical methods of quality control. The systematic structured approach to their introduction, which is recommended here, provides a powerful spearhead with which to improve the quality of conformance and consistency of manufactured goods. Increased knowledge of process capability will also assist in marketing decisions and product design.

The importance of the systematic use of statistical methods of process quality control in manufacturing industry cannot be over-emphasized. To compete internationally, both in home markets and overseas, companies must adopt a professional approach to the collection, analysis, and use of quality data.

Acknowledgement
The author would like to acknowledge the contribution of Dr Roy Followell to the preparation of this chapter. It is the outcome of several years' collaborative work in helping manufacturing companies to overcome the barriers to acceptance of SPC.

Appendices

Appendix A   The Normal Distribution

(Alternatively known as the Gaussian Distribution)

The mathematic equation to the normal curve is:

$$y = \frac{1}{\sigma\sqrt{2\pi}} e^{-(x-\bar{x})^2/2\sigma^2}$$

where y = height of curve at any point x along the scale of
the variable,

σ = standard deviation of the population,

$\bar{x}$ = average value of the variable for the distribution

e = base of Napierian logarithms ($e = 2.7183$)

π = ratio of circumference of a circle to its diameter ($\pi = 3.1429$)

If $z = (x - \bar{x})/\sigma$, then the equation becomes:

$$y = \frac{1}{\sqrt{2\pi}} e^{-z^2/2}$$

The constant $1/\sqrt{2\pi}$ has been chosen to ensure that the area under this curve is equal to unity, or probability 1.0. This allows the area under the curve between any two values of z to represent the probability that any item chosen at random will fall between the two values of z. The values given in Table A1 show the proportion of process output beyond a single specification limit that is z standard deviation units away from the process average. It must be remembered, of course that the process must be in statistical control and the variable must be normally distributed (see Chapter 5).

Probability Paper

A convenient way to examine variables data is to plot it in a cumulative form on probability paper. This enables the proportion of items outside a

Table A1   Proportions under the tail of the normal distribution

$Z = \dfrac{(x - \mu)}{\sigma}$	.00	.01	.02	.03	.04	.05	.06	.07	.08	.09
0.0	.5000	.4960	.4920	.4880	.4840	.4801	.4761	.4721	.4681	.4641
0.1	.4602	.4562	.4522	.4483	.4443	.4404	.4364	.4325	.4286	.4247
0.2	.4207	.4168	.4129	.4090	.4052	.4013	.3974	.3936	.3897	.3859
0.3	.3821	.3783	.3745	.3707	.3669	.3632	.3594	.3557	.3520	.3483
0.4	.3446	.3409	.3372	.3336	.3300	.3264	.3238	.3192	.3156	.3121
0.5	.3085	.3050	.3015	.2981	.2946	.2912	.2877	.2843	.2810	.2776
0.6	.2743	.2709	.2676	.2643	.2611	.2578	.2546	.2514	.2483	.2451
0.7	.2420	.2389	.2358	.2327	.2296	.2266	.2236	.2206	.2177	.2148
0.8	.2119	.2090	.2061	.2033	.2005	.1977	.1949	.1922	.1894	.1867
0.9	.1841	.1814	.1788	.1762	.1736	.1711	.1685	.1660	.1635	.1611
1.0	.1587	.1562	.1539	.1515	.1492	.1469	.1446	.1423	.1401	.1379
1.1	.1357	.1335	.1314	.1292	.1271	.1251	.1230	.1210	.1190	.1170
1.2	.1151	.1131	.1112	.1093	.1075	.1056	.1038	.1020	.1003	.0985
1.3	.0968	.0951	.0934	.0918	.0901	.0885	.0869	.0853	.0838	.0823
1.4	.0808	.0793	.0778	.0764	.0749	.0735	.0721	.0708	.0694	.0681
1.5	.0668	.0655	.0643	.0630	.0618	.0606	.0594	.0582	.0571	.0559
1.6	.0548	.0537	.0526	.0516	.0505	.0495	.0485	.0475	.0465	.0455
1.7	.0446	.0436	.0427	.0418	.0409	.0401	.0392	.0384	.0375	.0367
1.8	.0359	.0351	.0344	.0336	.0329	.0322	.0314	.0307	.0301	.0294
1.9	.0287	.0281	.0274	.0268	.0262	.0256	.0250	.0244	.0239	.0233
2.0	.0228	.0222	.0216	.0211	.0206	.0201	.0197	.0192	.0187	.0183
2.1	.0179	.0174	.0170	.0165	.0161	.0157	.0153	.0150	.0146	.0142

2.2	.0139	.0135	.0132	.0128	.0125	.0122	.0119	.0116	.0113	.0110
2.3	.0107	.0104	.0101	.0099	.0096	.0093	.0091	.0088	.0086	.0084
2.4	.0082	.0079	.0077	.0075	.0073	.0071	.0069	.0067	.0065	.0063
2.5	.0062	.0060	.0058	.0057	.0055	.0053	.0052	.0050	.0049	.0048
2.6	.0046	.0045	.0044	.0042	.0041	.0040	.0039	.0037	.0036	.0035
2.7	.0034	.0033	.0032	.0031	.0030	.0029	.0028	.0028	.0027	.0026
2.8	.0025	.0024	.0024	.0023	.0022	.0021	.0021	.0020	.0019	.0019
2.9	.0018	.0018	.0017	.0016	.0016	.0015	.0015	.0014	.0014	.0013
3.0	.0013									
3.1	.0009									
3.2	.0006									
3.3	.0004									
3.4	.0003									
3.5	.00025									
3.6	.00015									
3.7	.00010									
3.8	.00007									
3.9	.00005									
4.0	.00003									

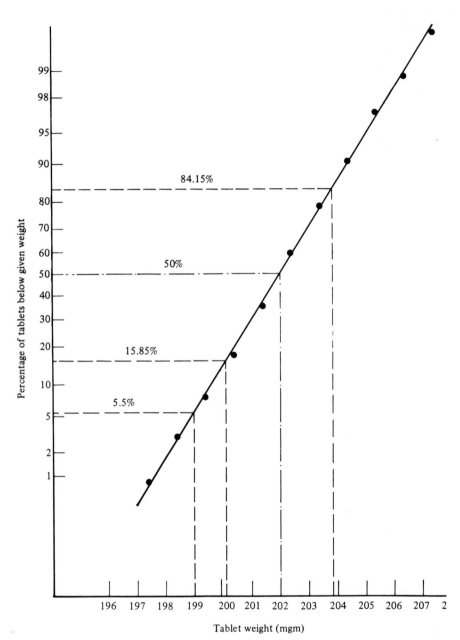

Fig. A.1   Probability paper plot of tablet weights

given limit to be read directly from the diagram. It also allows the data to be tested for normality – if it is normal the cumulative frequency plot will be a straight line.

The type of graph paper shown in Fig. A1 is readily obtainable from the Chartwell range (H.W. Peel and Co. Ltd, Greenford, Middlesex). The variable is marked along the linear horizontal scale, whilst the vertical scale shows the percentage of items with variables below that value. The method of using probability paper depends upon the number of values available.

Large Sample Size

Column 1 and 2 in Table A2 give a frequency table for weights of tablets. The cumulative total of tablets with the corresponding weights are given in Column 3. The cumulative totals are expressed as percentages of $(n + 1)$, where n is the total number of tablets, in column 4. These percentages are plotted against the upper boundaries of the class intervals on probability paper in Fig. A1. The points fall approximately on a straight line indicating that the distribution is Normal. From the graph, we can read, for example, that about 5.5 per cent of the tablets in the population weigh 199.0 mgm or less. This may be useful information if that weight represents a specification tolerance. We can also read off the median value as 202.0 mgm – a value below which half (50 per cent) of the tablet weights will lie. If the distribution is Normal, the median is also the average weight.

It is possible to estimate the standard deviation of the data, using Fig. A1. We know that 68.3% of the data from a Normal distribution will lie between the values $\mu \pm \sigma$. Consequently if we read off the tablet weights correspond-

Table A2   Table weights

Column 1 tablet weights (mgm)	Column 2 frequency (f)	Column 3 cumulative (i)	Column 4 percentage: $\left(\dfrac{i}{n+1}\right) \times 100$
196.5–197.4	3	3	0.82
197.5–198.4	8	11	3.01
198.5–199.4	18	29	7.92
199.5–200.4	35	64	17.49
200.5–201.4	66	130	35.52
201.5–202.4	89	219	59.84
202.5–203.4	68	287	78.42
203.5–204.4	44	331	90.44
204.5–205.4	24	355	96.99
205.5–206.4	7	362	98.91
206.5–207.4	3	365(n)	99.73

ing to 15.85 per cent and 84.15 per cent of the population, the difference between the two values will be equal to twice the standard deviation (σ).

Hence, from Fig. A1,

Weight at 84.15% = 203.85 mgm

Weight at 15.85% = 200.15 mgm

$$2\sigma = 3.70\,\text{mgm}$$
$$\sigma = 1.85\,\text{mgm}$$

Small Sample Size

The procedure for sample sizes of less than 20 is very similar. A sample of ten light bulbs have lives as shown in Table A3. Once again the cumulative number failed by a given life is computed (2nd column) and expressed as a percentage of $(n + 1)$ where n is the number of bulbs examined (3rd column). The results have been plotted on probability paper in Fig. A2. Estimates of mean and standard deviation may be made as before.

Non-Normality

Non-Normal distributions are indicated on probability paper by non-straight lines. In some cases, if the data is plotted on logarithmic probability paper, a straight line is obtained. This indicates that the data is taken from a log-Normal distribution, which may then be used to estimate the appropriate descriptive parameters.

Table A3   Lives of light bulbs

Bulb life in hours (ranked in ascending order)	Cumulative number of bulbs failed by a given Life (i)	Percentage: $\dfrac{i}{n+1} \times 100$
460	1	9.1
520	2	18.2
550	3	27.3
580	4	36.4
620	5	45.5
640	6	54.5
660	7	63.6
700	8	72.7
740	9	81.8
800	10(n)	90.9

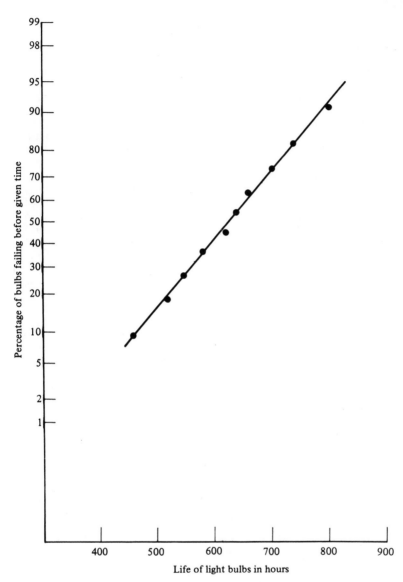

Fig. A.2   Probability paper plot of light bulb lives

Appendix B   Constants used in the design of control charts for mean

Sample Size (n)	*Hartley's Constant (d_n or d_2)*	*Constants for Mean Charts*						
		$A'_{.025}$	$A'_{.001}$	A_2	$A_{.025}$	$A_{.001}$	$A'''_{.025}$	$A'''_{.001}$
2	1.128	1.229	1.937	1.88	1.386	2.185	1.737	2.738
3	1.693	0.668	1.054	1.02	1.132	1.784	1.277	2.012
4	2.059	0.476	0.750	0.73	0.980	1.545	1.063	1.676
5	2.326	0.377	0.594	0.58	0.876	1.382	0.932	1.470
6	2.534	0.316	0.498	0.48	0.800	1.262	0.841	1.326
7	2.704	0.274	0.432	0.42	0.741	1.168	0.772	1.217
8	2.847	0.244	0.384	0.37	0.693	1.092	0.718	1.131
9	2.970	0.220	0.347	0.34	0.653	1.030	0.674	1.063
10	3.078	0.202	0.317	0.31	0.620	0.977	0.637	1.004
11	3.173	0.186	0.294	0.29	0.591	0.932	0.606	0.955
12	3.258	0.174	0.274	0.27	0.566	0.892	0.579	0.913
13					0.544	0.857	0.555	0.875
14					0.524	0.826	0.534	0.842
15					0.506	0.798	0.515	0.812
16					0.490	0.773	0.498	0.786
17					0.475	0.750	0.483	0.762
18					0.462	0.728	0.469	0.739
19					0.450	0.709	0.456	0.719
20					0.438	0.691	0.444	0.700
21					0.428	0.674	0.434	0.683
22					0.418	0.659	0.423	0.667
23					0.409	0.644	0.413	0.651
24					0.400	0.631	0.404	0.638
25					0.392	0.618	0.396	0.625

Formulae

$$\sigma = \frac{\bar{R}}{d_n} = \frac{\bar{R}}{d_2}$$

Mean Charts

Action Lines = $\bar{X} \pm A'_{.001}\bar{R}$ Warning Lines = $\bar{X} \pm A'_{.025}\bar{R}$

or $\bar{X} \pm A'_{.001}\sigma$ or $\bar{X} \pm A_{.025}\sigma$

or $\bar{X} \pm A'''_{.001}\bar{s}$ or $\bar{X} \pm A'''_{.025}\bar{s}$

Control Limit = $\bar{X} \pm A_2\bar{R}$

Appendix C Constants used in the design of control charts for range

Sample Size (n)	Constants for use with mean range ($\bar{R}$)				Constants for use with standard deviation (σ)				Constants for use in USA range charts	
	$D'_{.999}$	$D'_{.001}$	$D'_{.975}$	$D'_{.025}$	$D_{.999}$	$D_{.001}$	$D_{.975}$	$D_{.025}$	D_2	D_4
2	0.00	4.12	0.04	2.81	0.00	4.65	0.04	3.17	0	3.27
3	0.04	2.98	0.18	2.17	0.06	5.05	0.30	3.68	0	2.57
4	0.10	2.57	0.29	1.93	0.20	5.30	0.59	3.98	0	2.28
5	0.16	2.34	0.37	1.81	0.37	5.45	0.85	4.20	0	2.11
6	0.21	2.21	0.42	1.72	0.54	5.60	1.06	4.36	0	2.00
7	0.26	2.11	0.46	1.66	0.69	5.70	1.25	4.49	0.8	1.92
8	0.29	2.04	0.50	1.62	0.83	5.80	1.41	4.61	0.14	1.86
9	0.32	1.99	0.52	1.58	0.96	5.90	1.55	4.70	0.18	1.82
10	0.35	1.93	0.54	1.56	1.08	5.95	1.67	4.79	0.22	1.78
11	0.38	1.91	0.56	1.53	1.20	6.05	1.78	4.86	0.26	1.74
12	0.40	1.87	0.58	1.51	1.30	6.10	1.88	4.92	0.28	1.72

Formulae

Action Lines:	Upper	=	$D'_{.001}\bar{R}$	Lower	=	$D'_{.999}\bar{R}$
		or	$D_{.001}\sigma$		or	$D_{.999}\sigma$
Warning Lines:	Upper	=	$D'_{.025}\bar{R}$	Lower	=	$D'_{.975}\bar{R}$
		or	$D_{.025}\sigma$		or	$D_{.975}\sigma$
Control Limits:	Upper	=	$D_4\bar{R}$	Lower	=	D_2R

Appendix D   Tests for runs on control charts

Table D1   *Test for significance of runs – either side of the mean*

c = largest number of points on one side of mean
d = smallest number of points on other side of mean

The probability of obtaining an equal or lower number of runs than listed in the table is 0.005 for A (1 in 200) and 0.05 for B (1 in 20)

$c=$	6		7		8		9		10		11		12		13		14		15		16		17		18		19		20	
d	A	B	A	B	A	B	A	B	A	B	A	B	A	B	A	B	A	B	A	B	A	B	A	B	A	B	A	B	A	B
6	2	3	2	4	3	4	3	4	3	5	3	5	3	5	3	5	4	5	4	6	4	6	4	6	4	6	4	6	4	6
7			3	4	3	4	3	5	3	5	4	5	4	6	4	6	4	6	4	6	5	6	5	7	5	7	5	7	5	7
8					3	5	3	5	4	6	4	6	4	6	5	6	5	7	5	7	5	7	5	7	6	7	6	8	6	8
9							4	6	4	6	5	6	5	7	5	7	5	7	6	8	6	8	6	8	6	8	6	8	7	9
10									5	6	5	7	5	7	5	8	6	8	6	8	6	8	7	9	7	9	7	9	7	9
11											5	7	6	8	6	8	6	8	6	9	7	9	7	9	7	10	8	10	8	10
12													6	8	6	9	7	9	7	9	7	10	8	10	8	10	8	10	8	11
13															7	9	7	9	7	10	8	10	8	10	8	11	9	11	9	11
14																	7	10	8	10	8	11	8	11	9	11	9	12	9	12
15																			8	11	9	11	9	11	9	12	10	12	10	12
16																					9	11	9	12	10	12	10	13	10	13
17																							10	12	10	13	10	13	11	13
18																									11	13	11	14	11	14
19																											11	14	12	14
20																													12	15

Appendix D (contd.)

Table D2   Test for significance of length of runs
The probabilities of obtaining various run lengths from a given number of data points
(k) are given in the table

k	Run Length							
k	3	4	5	6	7	8	9
4	0.0833						
5		0.0167					
6		0.0306	0.0028				
7		0.0444		0.0004			
8		0.0583		0.0007			
9			0.0099	0.0011			
10			0.0123	0.0014			
11			0.0147	0.0018			
12			0.0170	0.0021			
13			0.0194	0.0025			
14			0.0217	0.0028			
15			0.0239	0.0032			
20			0.0355		0.0006		
40				0.0118	0.0015		
60				0.0186	0.0023		
80				0.0254	0.0032		
100				0.0322		0.0005	
200					0.0085	0.0010	
500					0.0215	0.0024	
1,000					0.0428		0.0005
5,000						0.0245	0.0025

Appendix E   Relative precision and relaxed control

Table E1   *The Relative Precision Index (RPI)*
– Minimum Values

Sample size n	Minimum value of RPI to avoid defectives
2	5.321
3	3.544
4	2.914
5	2.580
6	2.363
7	2.210
8	2.108
9	2.020

Formula: $RPI = 2T/\bar{R}$

Table E2   *Categories of process capability*

Sample size (n)	Value of RPI		
	High relative precision	Medium relative precision	Low relative precision
2	> 7.0	6.0 to 7.0	< 6.0
3	> 5.0	4.0 to 5.0	< 4.0
4	> 4.0	3.0 to 4.0	< 3.0
5 & 6	> 3.5	2.5 to 3.5	< 2.5

Table E3   *Constants used in the design of modified or relaxed control charts for*
sample mean

High precision class only

Sample size (n)	Up to 0.1% outside tolerances		Up to 0.01% outside tolerances	
	$A''_{0.025}$	$A''_{0.001}$	$A''_{0.025}$	$A''_{0.001}$
2	1.51	0.80	2.32	1.61
3	1.16	0.77	1.70	1.31
4	1.02	0.75	1.46	1.19
5	0.95	0.73	1.34	1.12
6	0.90	0.71	1.26	1.08

Formulae:

Upper Action Line $\;=$ Upper Tolerance $- A''_{.001}\bar{R}$
Upper Warning Line $=$ Upper Tolerance $- A''_{.025}\bar{R}$
Lower Warning Line $=$ Lower Tolerance $+ A''_{.025}\bar{R}$
Lower Action Line $\;=$ Lower Tolerance $+ A''_{.001}\bar{R}$

Appendix F   Constants used in the design of control charts for median and range

Sample size (n)	Constants for median charts		Constants for range charts	
	$A^m_{.001}$	$A^m_{.025}$	$D^m_{.001}$	$D^m_{.025}$
2	2.291	1.453	3.981	2.525
3	1.303	0.826	2.827	1.793
4	0.854	0.542	2.446	1.552
5	0.733	0.465	2.241	1.424
6	0.579	0.367	2.117	1.343
7	0.536	0.340	2.026	1.285
8	0.454	0.288	1.958	1.242
9	0.432	0.274	1.906	1.209
10	0.380	0.241	1.863	1.181

Formulae:

Median chart: Action lines $= = \tilde{X} \pm A^m_{.001}\tilde{R}$

Warning Lines $= = \tilde{X} \pm A^m_{.025}\tilde{R}$

Range chart: Upper Action Line $= D^m_{.001}\tilde{R}$

Upper Warning Line $= D^m_{.025}\tilde{R}$

Appendix G   Constants used in the design of control charts for standard deviation

Sample size (n)	C_n	$B'_{.001}$	$B'_{.025}$	$B'_{.975}$	$B'_{.999}$	$B_{.001}$	$B_{.025}$	$B_{.975}$	$B_{.999}$
2	1.253	4.117	2.802	0.039	0.016	3.286	2.236	0.031	0.013
3	1.128	2.963	2.170	0.179	0.036	2.627	1.924	0.159	0.032
4	1.085	2.522	1.911	0.291	0.098	2.324	1.761	0.268	0.090
5	1.064	2.282	1.780	0.369	0.161	2.145	1.673	0.347	0.151
6	1.051	2.128	1.694	0.429	0.215	2.025	1.612	0.408	0.205
7	1.042	2.005	1.614	0.471	0.263	1.924	1.549	0.452	0.252
8	1.036	1.930	1.567	0.509	0.303	1.863	1.513	0.491	0.292
9	1.032	1.866	1.527	0.538	0.337	1.808	1.480	0.522	0.327
10	1.028	1.809	1.491	0.563	0.368	1.760	1.450	0.548	0.358
11	1.025	1.775	1.485	0.582	0.394	1.732	1.449	0.568	0.384
12	1.023	1.729	1.442	0.603	0.417	1.690	1.410	0.589	0.408
13	1.021	1.690	1.422	0.619	0.439	1.655	1.393	0.606	0.430
14	1.019	1.673	1.407	0.632	0.458	1.642	1.381	0.620	0.449
15	1.018	1.639	1.395	0.645	0.474	1.610	1.370	0.634	0.466
16	1.017	1.625	1.375	0.656	0.490	1.598	1.352	0.645	0.482
17	1.016	1.605	1.362	0.668	0.504	1.580	1.341	0.657	0.496
18	1.015	1.586	1.350	0.676	0.518	1.563	1.330	0.666	0.510
19	1.014	1.570	1.342	0.687	0.529	1.548	1.323	0.678	0.522
20	1.013	1.540	1.337	0.689	0.537	1.520	1.320	0.680	0.530
21	1.013	1.522	1.325	0.701	0.551	1.503	1.308	0.692	0.544
22	1.012	1.509	1.317	0.708	0.562	1.491	1.301	0.700	0.555
23	1.011	1.497	1.309	0.715	0.569	1.481	1.295	0.707	0.563
24	1.011	1.488	1.302	0.720	0.578	1.472	1.288	0.712	0.572
25	1.011	1.475	1.295	0.726	0.586	1.459	1.281	0.718	0.580

Formulae $\sigma = \bar{s}c_n$

Standard Deviation Chart

$$\begin{cases} \text{Upper Action Line} & = B'_{.001}\bar{s} \quad \text{or} \quad B_{.001}\sigma \\ \text{Upper Warning Line} & = B'_{.025}\bar{s} \quad \text{or} \quad B_{.025}\sigma \\ \text{Lower Warning Line} & = B'_{.975}\bar{s} \quad \text{or} \quad B_{.975}\sigma \\ \text{Lower Action Line} & = B'_{.999}\bar{s} \quad \text{or} \quad B_{.999}\sigma \end{cases}$$

Appendix H   Cumulative Poisson probability tables

The table gives the probability that x or more defects (or defectives) will be found when the average number of defects (or defectives) is $\bar{c}$.

$\bar{c} =$	0.1	0.2	0.3	0.4	0.5	0.6	0.7	0.8	0.9	1.0
$x = 0$	1.0000	1.0000	1.0000	1.0000	1.0000	1.0000	1.0000	1.0000	1.0000	1.0000
1	.0952	.1813	.2592	.3297	.3935	.4512	.5034	.5507	.5934	.6321
2	.0047	.0175	.0369	.0616	.0902	.1219	.1558	.1912	.2275	.2642
3	.0002	.0011	.0036	.0079	.0144	.0231	.0341	.0474	.0629	.0803
4		.0001	.0003	.0008	.0018	.0034	.0058	.0091	.0135	.0190
5				.0001	.0002	.0004	.0008	.0014	.0023	.0037
6							.0001	.0002	.0003	.0006
7										.0001

$\bar{c} =$	1.1	1.2	1.3	1.4	1.5	1.6	1.7	1.8	1.9	2.0
$x = 0$	1.0000	1.0000	1.0000	1.0000	1.0000	1.0000	1.0000	1.0000	1.0000	1.0000
1	.6671	.6988	.7275	.7534	.7769	.7981	.8173	.8347	.8504	.8647
2	.3010	.3374	.3732	.4082	.4422	.4751	.5068	.5372	.5663	.5940
3	.0996	.1205	.1429	.1665	.1912	.2166	.2428	.2694	.2963	.3233
4	.0257	.0338	.0431	.0537	.0656	.0788	.0932	.1087	.1253	.1429
5	.0054	.0077	.0107	.0143	.0186	.0237	.0296	.0364	.0441	.0527
6	.0010	.0015	.0022	.0032	.0045	.0060	.0080	.0104	.0132	.0166
7	.0001	.0003	.0004	.0006	.0009	.0013	.0019	.0026	.0034	.0045
8			.0001	.0001	.0002	.0003	.0004	.0006	.0008	.0011
9							.0001	.0001	.0002	.0002

$\bar{c} =$	2.1	2.2	2.3	2.4	2.5	2.6	2.7	2.8	2.9	3.0
$x = 0$	1.0000	1.0000	1.0000	1.0000	1.0000	1.0000	1.0000	1.0000	1.0000	1.0000
1	.8775	.8892	.8997	.9093	.9179	.9257	.9328	.9392	.9450	.9502
2	.6204	.6454	.6691	.6916	.7127	.7326	.7513	.7689	.7854	.8009
3	.3504	.3773	.4040	.4303	.4562	.4816	.5064	.5305	.5540	.5768
4	.1614	.1806	.2007	.2213	.2424	.2640	.2859	.3081	.3304	.3528
5	.0621	.0725	.0838	.0959	.1088	.1226	.1371	.1523	.1682	.1847
6	.0204	.0249	.0300	.0357	.0420	.0490	.0567	.0651	.0742	.0839
7	.0059	.0075	.0094	.0116	.0142	.0172	.0206	.0244	.0287	.0335
8	.0015	.0020	.0026	.0033	.0042	.0053	.0066	.0081	.0099	.0119
9	.0003	.0005	.0006	.0009	.0011	.0015	.0019	.0024	.0031	.0038
10	.0001	.0001	.0001	.0002	.0003	.0004	.0005	.0007	.0009	.0011
11					.0001	.0001	.0001	.0002	.0002	.0003
12									.0001	.0001

$\bar{c} =$	3.1	3.2	3.3	3.4	3.5	3.6	3.7	3.8	3.9	4.0
$x = 0$	1.0000	1.0000	1.0000	1.0000	1.0000	1.0000	1.0000	1.0000	1.0000	1.0000
1	.9550	.9592	.9631	.9666	.9698	.9727	.9753	.9776	.9798	.9817
2	.8153	.8288	.8414	.8532	.8641	.8743	.8838	.8926	.9008	.9084
3	.5988	.6201	.6406	.6603	.6792	.6973	.7146	.7311	.7469	.7619
4	.3752	.3975	.4197	.4416	.4634	.4848	.5058	.5265	.5468	.5665
5	.2018	.2194	.2374	.2558	.2746	.2936	.3128	.3322	.3516	.3712
6	.0943	.1054	.1171	.1295	.1424	.1559	.1699	.1844	.1994	.2149
7	.0388	.0446	.0510	.0579	.0653	.0733	.0818	.0909	.1005	.1107
8	.0142	.0168	.0198	.0231	.0267	.0308	.0352	.0401	.0454	.0511
9	.0047	.0057	.0069	.0083	.0099	.0117	.0137	.0160	.0185	.0214

x =										
10	.0014	.0018	.0022	.0027	.0033	.0040	.0048	.0058	.0069	.0081
11	.0004	.0005	.0006	.0008	.0010	.0013	.0016	.0019	.0023	.0028
12	.0001	.0001	.0002	.0002	.0003	.0004	.0005	.0006	.0007	.0009
13				.0001	.0001	.0001	.0001	.0002	.0002	.0003
14									.0001	.0001

$\bar{c} =$	4.1	4.2	4.3	4.4	4.5	4.6	4.7	4.8	4.9	5.0
x = 0	1.0000	1.0000	1.0000	1.0000	1.0000	1.0000	1.0000	1.0000	1.0000	1.0000
1	.9834	.9850	.9864	.9877	.9889	.9899	.9909	.9918	.9926	.9933
2	.9155	.9220	.9281	.9337	.9389	.9437	.9482	.9523	.9561	.9596
3	.7762	.7898	.8026	.8149	.8264	.8374	.8477	.8575	.8667	.8753
4	.5858	.6046	.6228	.6406	.6577	.6743	.6903	.7058	.7207	.7350
5	.3907	.4102	.4296	.4488	.4679	.4868	.5054	.5237	.5418	.5595
6	.2307	.2469	.2633	.2801	.2971	.3142	.3316	.3490	.3665	.3840
7	.1214	.1325	.1442	.1564	.1689	.1820	.1954	.2092	.2233	.2378
8	.0573	.0639	.0710	.0786	.0866	.0951	.1040	.1133	.1231	.1334
9	.0245	.0279	.0317	.0358	.0403	.0451	.0503	.0558	.0618	.0681
10	.0095	.0111	.0129	.0149	.0171	.0195	.0222	.0251	.0283	.0318
11	.0034	.0041	.0048	.0057	.0067	.0078	.0090	.0104	.0120	.0137
12	.0011	.0014	.0017	.0020	.0024	.0029	.0034	.0040	.0047	.0055
13	.0003	.0004	.0005	.0007	.0008	.0010	.0012	.0014	.0017	.0020
14	.0001	.0001	.0002	.0002	.0003	.0003	.0004	.0005	.0006	.0007
15				.0001	.0001	.0001	.0001	.0001	.0002	.0002
16									.0001	.0001

Appendix H (Contd.)

$\bar{c} =$	5.2	5.4	5.6	5.8	6.0	6.2	6.4	6.6	6.8	7.0
$x =$ 0	1.0000	1.0000	1.0000	1.0000	1.0000	1.0000	1.0000	1.0000	1.0000	1.0000
1	.9945	.9955	.9963	.9970	.9975	.9980	.9983	.9986	.9989	.9991
2	.9658	.9711	.9756	.9794	.9826	.9854	.9877	.9897	.9913	.9927
3	.8912	.9052	.9176	.9285	.9380	.9464	.9537	.9600	.9656	.9704
4	.7619	.7867	.8094	.8300	.8488	.8658	.8811	.8948	.9072	.9182
5	.5939	.6267	.6579	.6873	.7149	.7408	.7649	.7873	.8080	.8270
6	.4191	.4539	.4881	.5217	.5543	.5859	.6163	.6453	.6730	.6993
7	.2676	.2983	.3297	.3616	.3937	.4258	.4577	.4892	.5201	.5503
8	.1551	.1783	.2030	.2290	.2560	.2840	.3127	.3419	.3715	.4013
9	.0819	.0974	.1143	.1328	.1528	.1741	.1967	.2204	.2452	.2709
10	.0397	.0488	.0591	.0708	.0839	.0984	.1142	.1314	.1498	.1695
11	.0177	.0225	.0282	.0349	.0426	.0514	.0614	.0726	.0849	.0985
12	.0073	.0096	.0125	.0160	.0201	.0250	.0307	.0373	.0448	.0534
13	.0028	.0038	.0051	.0068	.0088	.0113	.0143	.0179	.0221	.0270
14	.0010	.0014	.0020	.0027	.0036	.0048	.0063	.0080	.0102	.0128
15	.0003	.0005	.0007	.0010	.0014	.0019	.0026	.0034	.0044	.0057
16	.0001	.0002	.0002	.0004	.0005	.0007	.0010	.0014	.0018	.0024
17		.0001	.0001	.0001	.0002	.0003	.0004	.0005	.0007	.0010
18					.0001	.0001	.0001	.0001	.0002	.0004
19									.0001	.0001

$\bar{c} =$	7.2	7.4	7.6	7.8	8.0	8.2	8.4	8.6	8.8	9.0
$x =$ 0	1.0000	1.0000	1.0000	1.0000	1.0000	1.0000	1.0000	1.0000	1.0000	1.0000
1	.9993	.9994	.9995	.9996	.9997	.9997	.9998	.9998	.9998	.9999
2	.9939	.9949	.9957	.9964	.9970	.9975	.9979	.9982	.9985	.9988
3	.9745	.9781	.9812	.9839	.9862	.9882	.9900	.9914	.9927	.9938
4	.9281	.9368	.9446	.9515	.9576	.9630	.9677	.9719	.9756	.9788
5	.8445	.8605	.8751	.8883	.9004	.9113	.9211	.9299	.9379	.9450
6	.7241	.7474	.7693	.7897	.8088	.8264	.8427	.8578	.8716	.8843
7	.5796	.6080	.6354	.6616	.6866	.7104	.7330	.7543	.7744	.7932
8	.4311	.4607	.4900	.5188	.5470	.5746	.6013	.6272	.6522	.6761
9	.2973	.3243	.3518	.3796	.4075	.4353	.4631	.4906	.5177	.5443
10	.1904	.2123	.2351	.2589	.2834	.3085	.3341	.3600	.3863	.4126
11	.1133	.1293	.1465	.1648	.1841	.2045	.2257	.2478	.2706	.2940
12	.0629	.0735	.0852	.0980	.1119	.1269	.1429	.1600	.1780	.1970
13	.0327	.0391	.0464	.0546	.0638	.0739	.0850	.0971	.1102	.1242
14	.0159	.0195	.0238	.0286	.0342	.0405	.0476	.0555	.0642	.0739
15	.0073	.0092	.0114	.0141	.0173	.0209	.0251	.0299	.0353	.0415
16	.0031	.0041	.0052	.0066	.0082	.0102	.0125	.0152	.0184	.0220
17	.0013	.0017	.0022	.0029	.0037	.0047	.0059	.0074	.0091	.0111
18	.0005	.0007	.0009	.0012	.0016	.0021	.0027	.0034	.0043	.0053
19	.0002	.0003	.0004	.0005	.0006	.0009	.0011	.0015	.0019	.0024
20	.0001	.0001	.0001	.0002	.0003	.0003	.0005	.0006	.0008	.0011
21				.0001	.0001	.0001	.0002	.0002	.0003	.0004
22							.0001	.0001	.0001	.0002
23										.0001

Appendix H (Contd.)

$\bar{c} =$	9.2	9.4	9.6	9.8	10.0	11.0	12.0	13.0	14.0	15.0
$x =$ 0	1.0000	1.0000	1.0000	1.0000	1.0000	1.0000	1.0000	1.0000	1.0000	1.0000
1	.9999	.9999	.9999	.9999	1.0000	1.0000	1.0000	1.0000	1.0000	1.0000
2	.9990	.9991	.9993	.9994	.9995	.9998	.9999	1.0000	1.0000	1.0000
3	.9947	.9955	.9962	.9967	.9972	.9988	.9995	.9998	.9999	1.0000
4	.9816	.9840	.9862	.9880	.9897	.9951	.9977	.9990	.9995	.9998
5	.9514	.9571	.9622	.9667	.9707	.9849	.9924	.9963	.9982	.9991
6	.8959	.9065	.9162	.9250	.9329	.9625	.9797	.9893	.9945	.9972
7	.8108	.8273	.8426	.8567	.8699	.9214	.9542	.9741	.9858	.9924
8	.6990	.7208	.7416	.7612	.7798	.8568	.9105	.9460	.9684	.9820
9	.5704	.5958	.6204	.6442	.6672	.7680	.8450	.9002	.9379	.9626
10	.4389	.4651	.4911	.5168	.5421	.6595	.7576	.8342	.8906	.9301
11	.3180	.3424	.3671	.3920	.4170	.5401	.6528	.7483	.8243	.8815
12	.2168	.2374	.2588	.2807	.3032	.4207	.5384	.6468	.7400	.8152
13	.1393	.1552	.1721	.1899	.2084	.3113	.4240	.5369	.6415	.7324
14	.0844	.0958	.1081	.1214	.1355	.2187	.3185	.4270	.5356	.6368
15	.0483	.0559	.0643	.0735	.0835	.1460	.2280	.3249	.4296	.5343
16	.0262	.0309	.0362	.0421	.0487	.0926	.1556	.2364	.3306	.4319
17	.0135	.0162	.0194	.0230	.0270	.0559	.1013	.1645	.2441	.3359
18	.0066	.0081	.0098	.0119	.0143	.0322	.0630	.1095	.1728	.2511
19	.0031	.0038	.0048	.0059	.0072	.0177	.0374	.0698	.1174	.1805
20	.0014	.0017	.0022	.0028	.0035	.0093	.0213	.0427	.0765	.1248
21	.0006	.0008	.0010	.0012	.0016	.0047	.0116	.0250	.0479	.0830
22	.0002	.0003	.0004	.0005	.0007	.0023	.0061	.0141	.0288	.0531
23	.0001	.0001	.0002	.0002	.0003	.0010	.0030	.0076	.0167	.0327
24			.0001	.0001	.0001	.0005	.0010	.0040	.0093	.0195

$\bar{c}=$	25.0	24.0	23.0	22.0	21.0	20.0	19.0	18.0	17.0	16.0
25	.0112	.0050	.0020	.0007	.0002					
26	.0062	.0026	.0010	.0003	.0001					
27	.0033	.0013	.0005	.0001						
28	.0017	.0006	.0002	.0001						
29	.0009	.0003	.0001							
30	.0004	.0001								
31	.0002	.0001								
32	.0001									
$x=$ 0	1.0000	1.0000	1.0000	1.0000	1.0000	1.0000	1.0000	1.0000	1.0000	1.0000
1	1.0000	1.0000	1.0000	1.0000	1.0000	1.0000	1.0000	1.0000	1.0000	1.0000
2	1.0000	1.0000	1.0000	1.0000	1.0000	1.0000	1.0000	1.0000	1.0000	1.0000
3	1.0000	1.0000	1.0000	1.0000	1.0000	1.0000	1.0000	1.0000	1.0000	1.0000
4	1.0000	1.0000	1.0000	1.0000	1.0000	1.0000	1.0000	1.0000	1.0000	.9999
5	1.0000	1.0000	1.0000	1.0000	1.0000	1.0000	1.0000	.9999	.9998	.9996
6	1.0000	1.0000	1.0000	1.0000	1.0000	.9999	.9998	.9997	.9993	.9986
7	1.0000	1.0000	.9999	.9999	.9999	.9997	.9995	.9990	.9979	.9960
8	1.0000	1.0000	.9999	.9998	.9996	.9992	.9985	.9971	.9946	.9900
9	.9999	.9998	.9997	.9994	.9989	.9979	.9961	.9929	.9874	.9780
10	.9998	.9996	.9992	.9985	.9972	.9950	.9911	.9846	.9739	.9567
11	.9994	.9989	.9980	.9965	.9937	.9892	.9817	.9696	.9509	.9226
12	.9986	.9975	.9956	.9924	.9871	.9786	.9653	.9451	.9153	.8730
13	.9969	.9946	.9909	.9849	.9755	.9610	.9394	.9083	.8650	.8069
14	.9935	.9893	.9826	.9722	.9566	.9339	.9016	.8574	.7991	.7255
15	.9876	.9802	.9689	.9523	.9284	.8951	.8503	.7919	.7192	.6325
16	.9777	.9656	.9480	.9231	.8889	.8435	.7852	.7133	.6285	.5333
17	.9623	.9437	.9179	.8830	.8371	.7789	.7080	.6249	.5323	.4340
18	.9395	.9129	.8772	.8310	.7730	.7030	.6216	.5314	.4360	.3407
19	.9080	.8717	.8252	.7675	.6983	.6186	.5305	.4378	.3450	.2577

Appendix H   (Contd.)

$\bar{c}=$	16.0	17.0	18.0	19.0	20.0	21.0	22.0	23.0	24.0	25.0
20	.1878	.2637	.3491	.4394	.5297	.6157	.6940	.7623	.8197	.8664
21	.1318	.1945	.2693	.3528	.4409	.5290	.6131	.6899	.7574	.8145
22	.0892	.1385	.2009	.2745	.3563	.4423	.5284	.6106	.6861	.7527
23	.0582	.0953	.1449	.2069	.2794	.3595	.4436	.5277	.6083	.6825
24	.0367	.0633	.1011	.1510	.2125	.2840	.3626	.4449	.5272	.6061
25	.0223	.0406	.0683	.1067	.1568	.2178	.2883	.3654	.4460	.5266
26	.0131	.0252	.0446	.0731	.1122	.1623	.2229	.2923	.3681	.4471
27	.0075	.0152	.0282	.0486	.0779	.1174	.1676	.2277	.2962	.3706
28	.0041	.0088	.0173	.0313	.0525	.0825	.1225	.1726	.2323	.2998
29	.0022	.0050	.0103	.0195	.0343	.0564	.0871	.1274	.1775	.2366
30	.0011	.0027	.0059	.0118	.0218	.0374	.0602	.0915	.1321	.1821
31	.0006	.0014	.0033	.0070	.0135	.0242	.0405	.0640	.0958	.1367
32	.0003	.0007	.0018	.0040	.0081	.0152	.0265	.0436	.0678	.1001
33	.0001	.0004	.0010	.0022	.0047	.0093	.0169	.0289	.0467	.0715
34	.0001	.0002	.0005	.0012	.0027	.0055	.0105	.0187	.0314	.0498
35			.0002	.0006	.0015	.0032	.0064	.0118	.0206	.0338
36		.0001	.0001	.0003	.0008	.0018	.0038	.0073	.0132	.0225
37			.0001	.0002	.0004	.0010	.0022	.0044	.0082	.0146
38				.0001	.0002	.0005	.0012	.0026	.0050	.0092
39					.0001	.0003	.0007	.0015	.0030	.0057
40					.0001	.0001	.0004	.0008	.0017	.0034
41						.0001	.0002	.0004	.0010	.0020
42							.0001	.0002	.0005	.0012
43								.0001	.0003	.0007
44								.0001	.0002	.0004
45									.0001	.0002
46										.0001

$\bar{c} =$	26.0	27.0	28.0	29.0	30.0	32.0	34.0	36.0	38.0	40.0
$x =$ 9	1.0000	1.0000	1.0000	1.0000	1.0000	1.0000	1.0000	1.0000	1.0000	1.0000
10	.9999	.9999	1.0000	1.0000	1.0000	1.0000	1.0000	1.0000	1.0000	1.0000
11	.9997	.9998	.9999	1.0000	1.0000	1.0000	1.0000	1.0000	1.0000	1.0000
12	.9992	.9996	.9998	1.0000	1.0000	1.0000	1.0000	1.0000	1.0000	1.0000
13	.9982	.9990	.9994	.9997	.9998	1.0000	1.0000	1.0000	1.0000	1.0000
14	.9962	.9978	.9987	.9993	.9996	.9999	1.0000	1.0000	1.0000	1.0000
15	.9924	.9954	.9973	.9984	.9991	.9997	.9999	1.0000	1.0000	1.0000
16	.9858	.9912	.9946	.9967	.9981	.9993	.9998	.9999	1.0000	1.0000
17	.9752	.9840	.9899	.9937	.9961	.9986	.9995	.9998	1.0000	1.0000
18	.9580	.9726	.9821	.9885	.9927	.9972	.9990	.9997	.9999	1.0000
19	.9354	.9555	.9700	.9801	.9871	.9948	.9980	.9993	.9998	.9999
20	.9032	.9313	.9522	.9674	.9781	.9907	.9963	.9986	.9995	.9998
21	.8613	.8985	.9273	.9489	.9647	.9841	.9932	.9973	.9990	.9996
22	.8095	.8564	.8940	.9233	.9456	.9740	.9884	.9951	.9981	.9993
23	.7483	.8048	.8517	.8896	.9194	.9594	.9809	.9915	.9965	.9986
24	.6791	.7441	.8002	.8471	.8854	.9390	.9698	.9859	.9938	.9974
25	.6041	.6758	.7401	.7958	.8428	.9119	.9540	.9776	.9897	.9955
26	.5261	.6021	.6728	.7363	.7916	.8772	.9326	.9655	.9834	.9924
27	.4481	.5256	.6003	.6699	.7327	.8344	.9047	.9487	.9741	.9877
28	.3730	.4491	.5251	.5986	.6671	.7838	.8694	.9264	.9611	.9807
29	.3033	.3753	.4500	.5247	.5969	.7259	.8267	.8977	.9435	.9706
30	.2407	.3065	.3774	.4508	.5243	.6620	.7765	.8621	.9204	.9568
31	.1866	.2447	.3097	.3794	.4516	.5939	.7196	.8194	.8911	.9383
32	.1411	.1908	.2485	.3126	.3814	.5235	.6573	.7697	.8552	.9145
33	.1042	.1454	.1949	.2521	.3155	.4532	.5911	.7139	.8125	.8847
34	.0751	.1082	.1495	.1989	.2556	.3850	.5228	.6530	.7635	.8486
35	.0528	.0787	.1121	.1535	.2027	.3208	.4546	.5885	.7086	.8061
36	.0363	.0559	.0822	.1159	.1574	.2621	.3883	.5222	.6490	.7576
37	.0244	.0388	.0589	.0856	.1196	.2099	.3256	.4558	.5862	.7037
38	.0160	.0263	.0413	.0619	.0890	.1648	.2681	.3913	.5216	.6453

$\bar{c}=$	26.0	27.0	28.0	29.0	30.0	32.0	34.0	36.0	38.0	40.0
39	.0103	.0175	.0283	.0438	.0648	.1268	.2166	.3301	.4570	.5840
40	.0064	.0113	.0190	.0303	.0463	.0956	.1717	.2737	.3941	.5210
41	.0039	.0072	.0125	.0205	.0323	.0707	.1336	.2229	.3343	.4581
42	.0024	.0045	.0080	.0136	.0221	.0512	.1019	.1783	.2789	.3967
43	.0014	.0027	.0050	.0089	.0148	.0364	.0763	.1401	.2288	.3382
44	.0008	.0016	.0031	.0056	.0097	.0253	.0561	.1081	.1845	.2838
45	.0004	.0009	.0019	.0035	.0063	.0173	.0404	.0819	.1462	.2343
46	.0002	.0005	.0011	.0022	.0040	.0116	.0286	.0609	.1139	.1903
47	.0001	.0003	.0006	.0013	.0025	.0076	.0199	.0445	.0872	.1521
48	.0001	.0002	.0004	.0008	.0015	.0049	.0136	.0320	.0657	.1196
49		.0001	.0002	.0004	.0009	.0031	.0091	.0225	.0486	.0925
50			.0001	.0002	.0005	.0019	.0060	.0156	.0353	.0703
51			.0001	.0001	.0003	.0012	.0039	.0106	.0253	.0526
52				.0001	.0002	.0007	.0024	.0071	.0178	.0387
53					.0001	.0004	.0015	.0047	.0123	.0281
54					.0001	.0002	.0009	.0030	.0084	.0200
55						.0001	.0006	.0019	.0056	.0140
56						.0001	.0003	.0012	.0037	.0097
57							.0002	.0007	.0024	.0066
58							.0001	.0005	.0015	.0044
59							.0001	.0003	.0010	.0029
60								.0002	.0006	.0019
61								.0001	.0004	.0012
62								.0001	.0002	.0008
63									.0001	.0005
64									.0001	.0003
65										.0002
66										.0001
67										.0001

For values of $\bar{c}$ greater than 40, use the table of areas under the Normal curve (Appendix A) to obtain approximate Poisson probabilities, putting $\mu = \bar{c}$

Appendix I Problems for the Reader to Solve

1 (a) What is meant by 'quality' and by 'reliability'?
   (b) Differentiate between 'quality of design' and 'quality of conformance'
   (c) Briefly discuss the three costs which are usually associated with 'quality of conformance' and show how these vary with process capability.

2 'Quality' cannot be inspected into a product nor can it be advertised in, it must be designed and built in. – Discuss.

3 It has been argued that the definition of product quality as 'fitness for intended purpose' is more likely to lead to commercial success than is a definition such as 'conformance to specification'.

   Discuss the implications of these alternative definitions for the Quality Control function within a manufacturing enterprise.

4 You are a management consultant and have been asked to assist a manufacturing company in which fifteen per cent of the work force are final product inspectors. Currently, twenty per cent of the firm's output has to be reworked or scrapped. Write a report to the Managing Director of the company explaining, in general terms, how this situation arises and what steps may be taken to improve it.

5 The following quotations are from:
   On a clear day you can see General Motors by J. Patrick Wright:
   'I instituted a programme for testing and repairing faulty cars as they came off the assembly line – and the results were phenomenal. It cost about $8 a car, which drove The Fourteenth Floor up the wall. But I figured one way or the other we would end up fixing the defects or paying to have them fixed through recall campaigns or dealer warranty bills. If we caught the mistakes before the cars were delivered, we would get the reputation of building better quality products.....
   The internal corporation quality control audit revealed a 66% improvement in the quality of a Chevrolet coming off the assembly line between 1969 and 1973 models. And most important, warranty costs of our new cars were down substantially'.

   Explain the general principles behind this.

6 List and explain the usually accepted elements of 'quality costs'. Discuss how these elements are related to each other.

7   You are the Production Manager of a small engineering company and have just received the following memo:

MEMORANDUM
To: Production Manager
From: Sales Manager

SUBJECT: Order Number 2937/AZ

Joe Brown worked hard to get this order for us to manufacture 10,000 widgets for PQR Ltd. He now tells me that they are about to return the first batch of 1000 because many will not fit into the valve assembly that they tell us they are intended for. I must insist that you give rectification of this faulty batch number one priority, and that you make sure that this does not re-occur. As you know PQR Ltd are a new customer, and they could put a lot of work our way.

Incidentally I have heard that you have been sending a number of your operators on a training course in the use of the microbang widget gauge for use with that new machine of yours. I cannot help thinking that you should have spent the money on employing more finished product inspectors, rather than on training courses and high technology testing equipment.

a) Outline how you intend to investigate the causes of the 'faulty' widgets.
b) Discuss the final paragraph in the memo.

8   MEMORANDUM
To: Quality Manager
From: Managing Director

SUBJECT: *Quality Costs*

Below are the newly prepared quality costs for the last two quarters:

	last quarter 1985	first quarter 1986
Scrap and Rework	£ 15,600	£ 31,200
Customer returns/warranty	£ 26,200	£ 10,200
Total	£ 41,800	£ 41,400

Inspite of agreeing to your request to employ further inspection staff from January to increase finished product inspection to 100%, you will see that overall quality costs have shown no significant change. I look forward to receiving your comments on this.

Discuss the issues raised by the above memorandum.

9 Describe with examples the methods which are available for presenting information by means of charts, graphs, diagrams, etc.

10 The table below shows the recorded thicknesses of steel plates nominally .3" ± .01". Plot a frequency histogram of the plate thicknesses, and comment on the result.

Plate thicknesses (inches)

.2968	.2921	.2943	.3000	.2935	.3019
.2991	.2969	.2946	.2965	.2917	.3008
.3036	.3004	.2967	.2955	.2959	.2937
.2961	.3037	.2847	.2907	.2986	.2956
.2875	.2950	.2981	.1971	.3009	.2985
.3005	.3127	.2918	.2900	.3029	.3031
.3047	.2901	.2976	.3016	.2975	.2932
.3065	.3006	.3011	.3027	.2909	.2949
.3089	.2997	.3058	.2911	.2993	.2978
.2972	.2919	.2996	.2995	.3014	.2999

11 To establish a manufacturing specification for tablet thickness of a product, a sequence of 200 tablets was taken from the production stream and the thickness of each tablet was measured. The frequency distribution is shown below.

State and explain the conclusions you would draw from this distribution, assuming the following:

(a) the tablets came from one process
(b) the tablets came from two processes.

Measured thickness of tablets

Thickness (inch)	Number of tablets
0.238	2
.239	13
.240	32
.241	29
.242	18

Measured thickness of tablets (Contd.)

Thickness (inch)	Number of tablets
.243	21
.244	20
.245	22
.246	22
.247	13
.248	3
.249	0
.250	1
.251	1
.252	0
.253	1
.254	0
.255	2
	200

12 You have inherited, unexpectedly, a small engineering business which is both profitable and enjoys a full order book. You wish to be personally involved in this activity where the only area of immediate concern is the high levels of both scrap and re-work – costing together a sum equivalent to about 15% of the company's total sales.

Discuss your method of progressively picking-up, analyzing and solving this problem over a target period of 12 months. Illustrate any of the techniques you discuss.

13 Discuss in detail the applications of Pareto Analysis as an aid in solving production management problems. Give at least two illustrations.

14 You are responsible for a biscuit production plant, and are concerned about the output from one particular line which makes chocolate wholemeal biscuits. Output is consistently significantly below target. You suspect that this is because the line is frequently stopped, so you initiate an in-depth investigation over a typical two-week period. The table below shows the causes of the stoppages, number of occasions on which each occurred, and the average amount of output lost on each occasion.

Cause	No. of occurrences	Lost production (00's biscuits)
WRAPPING:		
Cellophane wrap breakage	1031	3
cartonner failure	85	100
ENROBER:		
chocolate too thin	102	1
chocolate too thick	92	3
PREPARATION:		
underweight biscuits	70	25
overweight biscuits	21	25
biscuits mis-shapen	58	1
OVENS:		
biscuits overcooked	87	2
biscuits undercooked	513	1

Use this data and an appropriate technique to indicate where to concentrate remedial action.

15 A company manufactures a range of domestic electrical appliances. Particular concern is being expressed about the warranty claims on one particular product. The customer service department provides the following data relating the claims to the unit/component part of the product which caused the claim:

Unit/component part	Number of claims	Average cost of warranty work (per claim)
Drum	110	48.1
Casing	12842	1.2
Work–top	142	2.7
Pump	246	8.9
Electric motor	798	48.9
Heater unit	621	15.6
Door lock mechanism	18442	0.8
Stabiliser	692	2.9
Powder additive unit	7562	1.2
Electric control unit	652	51.9
Switching mechanism	4120	10.2

Discuss what criteria are of importance in identifying those units/component parts to examine initially. Carry out full Pareto Analyses to identify such units/component parts.

16   The manufacturer of a domestic electrical appliance has been examining causes of warranty claims. Ten have been identified and the annual cost of warranty work resulting from these is as follows:

Cause	Annual cost of warranty work (£)
A	1090
B	2130
C	30690
D	620
E	5930
F	970
G	49980
H	1060
I	4980
J	3020

Carry out a Pareto Analysis on the above data, and suggest which causes you would tackle first.

17   The principal causes of accidents, their percentage of occurrence, and the estimated resulting loss of production per annum in the UK is given in the Table.

Table

Accident cause	Percentage of all accidents	Estimated Loss of production (£ million/annum)
Machinery	16	190
Transport	8	30
Falls from heights > 6′	16	100
Tripping	3	10
Striking against objects	9	7
Falling objects	7	20
Handling goods	27	310
Hand tools	7	65
Burns (including chemical)	5	15
Unspecified	2	3

(a) Using the appropriate data draw a Pareto curve and suggest how this may be used most effectively to tackle the problems of accident prevention.

(b) Give three other uses of Pareto analysis in manufacturing and explain briefly, in each case, how use of the technique helps the Production Manager.

18 'The only way to guarantee product quality is by 100% inspection.' Discuss.

19 What difficulties are likely to arise in attempting to apply 100% inspection for quality? Suggest ways in which these difficulties might be overcome.

20 'Statistical Process Control has developed into a substantial science in its own right'. Comment on this statement with reference to quality measurement and its application.

21 What is meant by the inherent variability of a process?

22 Process control charts may be classified under two broad headings, 'variables' and 'attributes'. Compare these two categories and indicate when each one may be most appropriate.

23 State the Central Limit Theorem and explain how it is used in Statistical Process Control.

24 A machine is constructed to produce ball bearings having a mean diameter of 0.574 in. and a standard deviation of 0.008 in. To determine whether the machine is in proper working order a sample of 6 ball bearings are taken every 2 hours and the mean diameter is computed from the sample.

(a) Design a decision rule whereby one can be fairly certain that the quality of the products is conforming to required results.
(b) Show how to represent graphically the decision rule in (a).

25 Specimens of concrete, collected daily from the work of a sub-contractor, yielded the results for compressive strength given below.

Set out these results on a quality control chart. Comment on the results and state whether, on the evidence available, the sub-contractor has met the minimum specification of 4000 p.s.i. for compressive strength.

Compressive strength (in 100's p.s.i.)

| Date | Specimen number | | | | |
	1	2	3	4	5
Feb. 1.	46.0	43.5	43.1	47.3	45.1
2.	45.0	45.7	40.9	44.0	43.6
3.	42.0	47.3	44.5	45.6	48.0
4.	49.1	45.7	46.4	46.0	47.1
8.	47.1	44.2	49.6	45.1	47.4
9.	43.1	44.4	43.4	45.8	46.4
10.	41.2	45.5	45.9	46.5	43.8
11.	41.0	46.7	43.3	49.4	48.0
15.	45.4	43.7	47.3	44.8	49.2
16.	40.0	43.1	48.3	44.5	46.7
17.	45.2	46.7	47.3	47.1	49.8
18.	44.2	43.5	45.0	44.0	44.7

26 The following are measures of the impurity, iron, in a fine chemical which is to be used in pharmaceutical manufacture. The data is given in parts per million (ppm)

Sample	X_1	X_2	X_3	X_4	X_5
1	15	11	8	15	6
2	14	16	11	14	7
3	13	6	9	5	10
4	15	15	9	15	7
5	9	12	9	8	8
6	11	14	11	12	5
7	13	12	9	6	10
8	10	15	12	4	6
9	8	12	14	9	10
10	10	10	9	14	14
11	13	16	12	15	18
12	7	10	9	11	16
13	11	7	16	10	14
14	11	7	10	10	7
15	13	9	12	13	17
16	17	10	11	9	8
17	4	14	5	11	11
18	8	9	6	13	9
19	9	10	7	10	13
20	15	10	12	12	16

Set up mean and range charts for controlling purity in the future.

27 (a) Describe the various components of 'total quality related cost' and explain how they are inter-related.

(b) You are responsible for a small plant which manufactures and packs jollytots, a children's sweet. The average contents of each packet should be 35 sugar-coated balls of candy which melt in your mouth.

Every half hour a random sample of five packets is taken, and the contents counted. These figures are shown below:

Sample	packet contents				
	1	2	3	4	5
1	33	36	37	38	36
2	35	35	32	37	35
3	31	38	35	36	38
4	37	35	36	36	34
5	34	35	36	36	37
6	34	33	38	35	38
7	34	36	37	35	34
8	36	37	35	32	31
9	34	34	32	34	36
10	34	35	37	34	32
11	34	34	35	36	32
12	35	35	41	38	35
13	36	36	37	31	34
14	35	35	32	32	39
15	35	35	34	34	34
16	33	33	35	35	34
17	34	40	36	32	37
18	33	35	33	34	40
19	34	33	37	34	34
20	37	32	34	35	34

Use the data to set up mean and range charts, and briefly outline their usage.

You are given; for $n = 5$,

$A'_{0.025} = 0.377$ $A'_{0.001} = 0.594$
$D'_{.999} = 0.16$, $D'_{.975} = 0.37$, $D'_{0.025} = 1.81$,
$D'_{0.001} = 2.34$ $d_n = 2.33$

28 You are responsible for a production line producing an item, the weight of which is a crucial parameter. The grand mean from 20

samples of size 4 is 1000 grams, and the mean range of the samples is 40 grams. From statistical tables, the values of the constants for setting up control charts are:

Mean Chart: $A'_{.001} = 0.750$, $A'_{.025} = 0.476$
Range Chart: $D'_{.001} = 2.57$, $D'_{.025} = 1.93$

Calculate the Action and Warning Lines for the mean and range chart and explain briefly how the chart would be operated.

29   Using process capability studies, processes may be classified into three categories. Explain the basis of this classification and, for each category, the implications for the production manager.

30   Conventional control charts are to be used on a process manufacturing steel pins with a length of 60 mm ± 1.5 mm. Two identical machines are involved in making the pins and process capability studies carried out on them reveal the following data:

Sample Size, $n = 5$.

| | Machine I | | Machine II | |
Sample No.	Mean	Range	Mean	Range
1	60.10	2.5	60.86	0.5
2	59.92	2.2	59.10	0.4
3	60.37	3.0	60.32	0.6
4	59.91	2.2	60.05	0.2
5	60.01	2.4	58.95	0.3
6	60.18	2.7	59.12	0.7
7	59.67	1.7	58.80	0.5
8	60.57	3.4	59.68	0.4
9	59.68	1.7	60.14	0.6
10	59.55	1.5	60.96	0.3
11	59.98	2.3	61.05	0.2
12	60.22	2.7	60.84	0.2
13	60.54	3.3	61.01	0.5
14	60.68	3.6	60.82	0.4
15	59.24	0.9	59.14	0.6
16	59.48	1.4	59.01	0.5
17	60.20	2.7	59.08	0.1
18	60.27	2.8	59.25	0.2
19	59.57	1.5	61.50	0.3
20	60.49	3.2	61.42	0.4

Calculate the control limits to be used on a mean and range chart for each machine and give the reasons for any differences between them.

Compare the results from each machine with the appropriate control chart limits and the specification tolerances.

Discuss the implications for action by the process management.

31 The following *averages* and *ranges* are for the lengths (in mm) of tubes used in pneumatic pumps. The sample size used is 5.

Sample No.	Average	Range
1	51.32	.20
2	51.29	.23
3	51.29	.04
4	51.23	.27
5	51.35	.26
6	51.23	.19
7	51.31	.28
8	51.34	.21
9	51.26	.36
10	51.27	.23
11	51.35	.13
12	51.30	.19
13	51.33	.25
14	51.29	.10
15	51.34	.15
16	51.39	.10
17	51.26	.13
18	51.35	.28
19	51.37	.09
20	51.32	.08

(i) Draw the control chart for sample means and the control chart for sample ranges from the given data and then plot the sample data on the charts.

(ii) Comment on the state of control.

32 The following data was obtained when measurements of the zinc concentration (measured as % zinc sulphate on sodium sulphate) were made in a viscose rayon spin-bath. The mean and range values of twenty samples of size 5 are given in the table.

Sample	Zn conc. %	Range %	Sample	Zn conc. %	Range %
1	6.97	0.38	11	7.05	0.23
2	6.93	0.20	12	6.92	0.21
3	7.02	0.36	13	7.00	0.28
4	6.93	0.31	14	6.99	0.20
5	6.94	0.28	15	7.08	0.16
6	7.04	0.20	16	7.04	0.17
7	7.03	0.38	17	6.97	0.25
8	7.04	0.25	18	7.00	0.23
9	7.01	0.18	19	7.07	0.19
10	6.99	0.29	20	6.96	0.25

If the data is to be used to initiate mean and range charts for controlling the process, determine the action and warning lines for the charts. What would your reaction be to the development chemist setting a tolerance of $7.00 \pm 0.25\%$ on the Zinc concentration in the spin-bath?

33 A manufacturer of a certain type of resistors decided to set up quality control charts for his product. Twenty-five samples of size 4 were taken. The mean and range of each sample are shown below. Construct Shewhart mean and range charts for the process and determine whether the process is under control.

Sample no.	Resistance (ohms)		Sample no.	Resistance (ohms)	
	Mean $\bar{x}$	Range $\bar{R}$		Mean $\bar{x}$	Range $\bar{R}$
1	122	10	15	120	13
2	126	6	16	125	12
3	118	5	17	118	5
4	121	8	18	119	8
5	126	11	19	124	4
6	125	5	20	121	3
7	119	4	21	125	7
8	121	3	22	121	5
9	124	11	23	120	4
10	125	14	24	121	4
11	123	10	25	119	6
12	124	9			
13	122	7		$\sum \bar{x} = 3050$	$\sum \bar{R} = 185$
14	121	11			

34 A dimension is specified as $0.825'' \pm 0.005''$. The following values of mean $\bar{x}$ and range R were obtained from samples of 4 parts taken from the process at half-hour intervals (all values in inches).

Sample no.	$\bar{x}$	R	Sample no.	$\bar{x}$	R
1	0.8220	0.0004	9	0.8251	0.0005
2	0.8228	0.0007	10	0.8253	0.0013
3	0.8233	0.0005	11	0.8257	0.0003
4	0.8232	0.0010	12	0.8257	0.0008
5	0.8235	0.0011	13	0.8265	0.0011
6	0.8241	0.0012	14	0.8260	0.0010
7	0.8244	0.0014	15	0.8270	0.0007
8	0.8248	0.0004			

Derive suitable control chart limits for controlling the mean of this process.

35 (a) Distinguish between random and assignable causes of variability in a manufacturing process.

(b) The diameters of 20 samples of five steel rods were measured to the nearest 0.01 mm. The mean and range of each sample are given below:

Sample No.	1	2	3	4	5
Mean (mm)	5.49	5.52	5.51	5.55	5.51
Range (mm)	0.04	0.09	0.09	0.06	0.05

Sample No.	6	7	8	9	10
Mean (mm)	5.51	5.49	5.51	5.52	5.49
Range (mm)	0.06	0.11	0.09	0.09	0.08

Sample No.	11	12	13	14	15
Mean (mm)	5.52	5.49	5.51	5.50	5.49
Range (mm)	0.08	0.04	0.09	0.07	0.07

Sample No.	16	17	18	19	20
Mean (mm)	5.53	5.53	5.51	5.49	5.50
Range (mm)	0.06	0.08	0.09	0.10	0.06

Calculate suitable control limits for process control charts. Comment on the state of control of the process.

(c) The design department have indicated that the specification for the rod diameters should be 5.5 ± 0.2 mm. Assess the relative precision of the process used to manufacture the rods. Use this information to decide if you would adjust at all the control chart limits designed in (b). Make any adjustments you decide are necessary and describe how the control charts would be used.

36 Twenty samples of five machined items were taken periodically from production and the inside diameter of a hole in each was measured to the nearest 0.01 mm. Calculate suitable control limits which could be used on charts to monitor the mean and the inherent variability of the diameters. State three decision rules that could be applied to a means chart with these limits.

The items were to be used subsequently in an assembly and specification values of 17.5 ± 0.2 mm were put onto the hole diameter. Assess the Relative Precision of the process used to machine the holes. In the light of this additional information, would you alter any of the limits you have calculated in (b). Give reasons for your answer.

Plot the 20 samples on control charts with new limits, if you thought these appropriate, or with the existing limits, and comment on the process.

Sample No.	1	2	3	4	5	6	7
Mean	17.510	17.524	17.486	17.522	17.492	17.506	17.500
Range	0.09	0.09	0.08	0.08	0.04	0.09	0.07

Sample No.	8	9	10	11	12	13	14
Mean	17.494	17.506	17.514	17.548	17.506	17.516	17.490
Range	0.11	0.06	0.05	0.06	0.09	0.09	0.04

Sample No.	15	16	17	18	19	20
Mean	17.528	17.510	17.486	17.498	17.530	17.490
Range	0.08	0.09	0.10	0.06	0.06	0.07

37 Describe the characteristics of the Normal Distribution and construct an example to show how these may be used in answering questions that arise from discussion of specification limits for a product.

38 The bottle filling machine at Peter's Sauces is being used to fill 15 oz bottles of their Spicy Sauce. The actual bottles will hold 15.6 oz. The machine has been set to discharge an average of 15.2 oz. It is known that the amount discharged follows a normal distribution with a standard distribution of 0.2 oz.

(i) What proportion of the bottles overflow?
(ii) The overflowing of bottles causes considerable problems and it has therefore been suggested that the average discharge should be adjusted to 15.1 oz. However in order to meet weights and measures regulations no more than 1 in 40 bottles, on average, must contain less than 14.6 oz. If the average discharge is adjusted to 15.1 oz are the weights and measures regulations being contravened?

39 In a cigarette-making process the specifications demand that the individual cigarette weight shall be below the nominal weight of 1.2 grams on only one occasion in 100. At present the cigarette-making machine produces to any required mean cigarette weight with a standard deviation of .01 gram. A new cigarette-making machine is available which makes to a more consistent weight, the standard deviation of weights being .008 gram. Both machines can make 2,000 cigarettes per minute, and will be required to operate for a 40 hour week 50 weeks per year. Tobacco costs £20 per kilogram. Find the annual saving made possible by the new machine and compare it to the new machine purchase price of £25,000.

40 What do you understand by the 'Average Run Length' of a Control Chart? A process, when in a stable condition, has a mean of 40 and a standard deviation of 3. Specify action and warning limits for mean and range of samples of six on a chart to control the process.
    Considering the means chart only, what is the average run length:
(a) When the process mean is 40?
(b) When the process mean is 36?
assuming the variance is unchanged.

41 (a) What is meant by the Average Run Length of a control chart for variables? For a Shewhart chart for means of samples of six with action lines only, what is the average run length:

(i) With the mean at the target value
(ii) After the mean has shifted by two standard deviations from the target value.

(b) Describe in detail one method of operating a cumulative sum chart such that a statistically based decision can be reached as to whether the process mean has changed. Under what circumstances is a cumulative sum chart preferable to a Shewhart chart for control of process mean.

42   Describe the procedure for assessing process capability with particular reference to the use of arithmetical probability graph paper.

Seventy-three samples of five components were measured with the following results.

Length (mm)	freq.
133.5–136.4	4
136.5–139.4	8
139.5–142.4	17
142.5–145.4	35
145.5–148.4	66
148.5–181.4	89
151.5–154.4	68
154.5–157.4	44
157.5–160.4	24
160.5–163.4	7
163.5–166.4	3

(i) State the class interval
(ii) Using plotting points of $\frac{i}{n+1}$ where i is the cumulative frequency to the i'th class and n is the total frequency, draw the distribution on to arithmetical probability graph paper.
(iii) The specification limits for the length are 140 mm $\pm$ 18 mm. Comment on the capability of the process.
(iv) Show that the percentage of components that have to be recut at this setting is approximately 9.

43   A chocolate manufacturer takes a sample of six boxes at the end of each hour in order to verify the weight of the chocolates contained within each box. The individual chocolates are also examined visually during the check-weighing and the various types of major and minor faults are counted.

The manufacturer equates 1 major fault to 4 minor faults and accepts a maximum equivalent to 2 minor physical faults/chocolate, in any box. Each box contains 24 chocolates.

Discuss any two control chart techniques which could be used to monitor the physical defects. Illustrate both how the charts would be set up and used.

Compare the characteristics of the two chosen techniques.

44   In the context of quality control explain what is meant by a *number of defectives* chart.

45   Explain the difference between an:

np-chart,
p-chart,
c-chart.

46   Write down the formulae for the probability of obtaining r defectives in a sample of size n drawn from a population proportion p defective based on:

(i) The Binomial distribution
(ii) The Poisson distribution

47   A factory finds that on average 20% of the bolts produced by a machine are defective. Determine the probability that out of 4 bolts chosen at random:

(a) 1, (b) 0, (c) at most 2 bolts will be defective.

48   A control chart for a new kind of plastic is to be initiated. Twenty-five samples of 100 plastic sheets from the assembly line were inspected for flaws during a pilot run. The results are given below. Set up the chart

Sample No.	1	2	3	4	5	6	7	8		
No. of flaws/sheet	2	3	0	2	4	2	8	4		
Sample No.	9	10	11	12	13	14	15	16	17	
No. of flaws/sheet	5	8	3	5	2	3	1	2	3	
Sample No.	18	19	20	21	22	23	24	25		
No. of flaws/sheet	4	1	0	3	2	4	2	1		

49   Twenty samples of 50 polyurethane foam products are selected.

The sample results are:

Sample No.	1	2	3	4	5	6	7	8	9	10
Number defective	2	3	1	4	0	1	2	2	3	2
Sample No.	11	12	13	14	15	16	17	18	19	20
Number defective	2	2	3	4	5	1	0	0	1	2

Design an np chart.
Plot these values on the chart and interpret the results.

50   In the table below are given the results from the inspection of filing cabinets for scratches and small indentations.

Cabinet No.	1	2	3	4	5	6	7	8	
Number of Defects	1	0	3	6	3	3	4	5	

Cabinet No.	9	10	11	12	13	14	15	16	
Number of Defects	10	8	4	3	7	5	3	1	

Cabinet No.	17	18	19	20	21	22	23	24	25
Number of Defects	4	1	1	1	0	4	5	5	5

Set up a control chart to monitor the number of defects. What is the average run length to detection when 6 defects are present?

Plot the data on the chart and comment upon the process. Plot the data on a suitably designed cusum chart and compare the two forms of presentation.

51   The following record shows the number of defective items found in a sample of 100 taken twice per day.

Sample no.	Number of defectives	Sample no.	Number of defectives
1	4	21	2
2	2	22	1
3	4	23	0
4	3	24	3
5	2	25	2
6	6	26	0
7	3	27	1
8	1	28	3
9	1	29	0
10	5	30	3
11	4	31	0
12	4	32	2
13	1	33	1
14	2	34	1
15	1	35	4
16	4	36	0
17	1	37	2
18	0	38	3
19	3	39	2
20	4	40	1

Set up and plot a cusum chart. Interpret your findings. (Assume a target value of 2 defectives.)

52 Explain the principle of (a) Shewhart control charts for sample mean and sample range, and (b) cumulative sum charts. Compare the performance of the two types of chart by plotting the following data and interpreting the results.

Sample no.	Data	Mean	Range
1	58, 60, 61, 58, 63	60.0	5
2	60, 58, 58, 60, 64	60.0	6
3	63, 59, 65, 62, 60	61.8	6
4	58, 60, 59, 61, 58	59.2	3
5	58, 62, 61, 59, 62	60.4	4
6	59, 60, 62, 58, 59	59.6	4
7	60, 62, 61, 57, 60	60.0	5
8	63, 61, 60, 59, 58	60.2	5
9	60, 63, 61, 61, 58	60.6	5
10	61, 59, 62, 59, 57	59.6	5
11	58, 59, 60, 59, 59	59.0	2
12	59, 59, 63, 62, 62	61.0	4
13	61, 60, 58, 63, 60	60.4	5
14	59, 58, 61, 59, 62	59.8	4
15	60, 61, 62, 61, 60	60.8	2
16	61, 59, 60, 61, 61	60.4	2
17	59, 59, 60, 60, 60	59.6	1
18	61, 56, 60, 61, 60	59,6	5
19	59, 62, 59, 57, 60	59.4	5
20	63, 63, 62, 59, 62	61.8	4
21	62, 60, 58, 62, 58	60.0	4
22	62, 57, 61, 59, 61	60.0	5
23	57, 61, 64, 58, 62	60.4	7
24	62, 60, 57, 61, 60	60.0	5
25	62, 62, 60, 60, 62	61.2	2
26	61, 60, 58, 59, 60	59.6	3
27	58, 61, 58, 61, 62	60.0	4
28	61, 62, 60, 60, 63	61.2	3
29	61, 58, 63, 61, 61	60.8	5
30	59, 63, 62, 62, 58	60.8	5
31	63, 59, 60, 61, 60	60.6	4
32	59, 60, 62, 61, 61	60.6	3
33	65, 63, 65, 63, 62	63.6	3
34	62, 60, 62, 61, 61	61.2	2

Sample no.	Data	Mean	Range
35	61, 65, 60, 61, 58	61.0	7
36	61, 59. 61, 62, 62	61.0	3
37	61, 65, 60, 61, 60	61.4	5
38	58, 62, 62, 59, 60	60.2	4
39	60, 59, 62, 58, 62	60.2	4
40	59, 61, 57, 64, 59	60.0	7
41	62, 61, 61, 59, 63	61.2	4
42	62, 58, 63, 59, 61	60.6	5
43	64, 61, 61, 62, 59	61.4	5
44	58, 58, 62, 63, 61	60.4	5
45	59, 64, 65, 61, 63	62.4	6
46	63, 63, 63, 66, 61	63.2	5
47	66, 64, 66, 63, 59	63.6	7
48	61, 65, 66, 63, 64	63.8	5
49	63, 59, 61, 65, 62	62.0	6
50	65, 66, 65, 65, 62	64.6	4

53 (a) The table below gives the average width (mm) for each of 20 samples of five lithographic plates. Also given is the range (mm) of each sample.

Sample no.	Mean	Range	Sample No.	Mean	Range
1	550.8	4.2	11	553.1	3.8
2	552.7	4.2	12	551.7	3.1
3	553.9	6.7	13	561.2	3.5
4	555.8	4.7	14	554.2	3.4
5	553.8	3.2	15	552.3	5.8
6	547.5	5.8	16	552.9	1.6
7	550.9	0.7	17	562.9	2.7
8	552.0	5.9	18	559.4	5.4
9	553.7	9.5	19	555.8	1.7
10	557.3	1.9	20	547.6	6.7

Calculate the control chart limits for the Shewhart Charts and plot the values on the charts. Interpret the results.

(b) The customer for the lithographic plates being manufactured in (a) has stipulated that each plate must fall within the specification tolerance limits of 540 mm ± 5 mm. If the process has the same *precision* as that described by the results in (a), comment on the process capability. Quantify any statements which you make.

(c) Design a cumulative sum (cusum) chart to control the process described in part (a). Explain the differences between this chart and the Shewhart chart.

54 Shewhart charts are to be used to maintain control on dissolved iron content of a dyestuff formulation in parts per million (ppm). After 25 subgroups of 5 measurements have been obtained,

$$\sum_{i=1}^{i=25} \bar{x}_i = 390 \quad \text{and} \quad \sum_{i=1}^{i=25} R_i = 84$$

where
$$\bar{x}_i = \text{mean of ith subgroup}$$
$$R_i = \text{range of ith subgroup.}$$

Design the appropriate control charts.

The specification on the process requires that no more than 18 ppm dissolved iron be present in the formulation. Assuming a normal distribution and that the process continues to be in statistical control with no change in average or dispersion, what proportion of the individual measurements may be expected to exceed this specification?

Design an appropriate cusum chart for control of the process mean and describe how the chart might be used in continuous production for product screening.

55 The following data was obtained when measurements were made on the dimension of steel balls for use in bearings. The mean and range values of sixteen samples of size five are given in the table:

Sample no.	Mean dia. (0.001")	Sample range (")	Sample no.	Mean dia. (0.001")	Sample range (")
1	250.2	0.005	9	250.4	0.004
2	251.3	0.005	10	250.0	0.004
3	250.4	0.005	11	249.4	0.0045
4	250.2	0.003	12	249.8	0.0035
5	250.7	0.004	13	249.3	0.0045
6	248.9	0.004	14	249.1	0.0035
7	250.2	0.005	15	251.0	0.004
8	249.1	0.004	16	250.6	0.0045

Is the process in statistical control?

Design a mean cusum chart for the process and plot the results on the chart.

Interpret the cusum chart and explain briefly how it may be used to categorise production in pre-selection for an operation in the assembly of the bearings.

56 The data given below are taken from a process of acceptable mean value $\mu_0 = 8.0$ and unacceptable mean value $\mu_1 = 7.5$ and known standard deviation of 0.45.

Sample no.	x	Sample no.	$\bar{x}$
1	8.04	11	8.11
2	7.84	12	7.80
3	8.46	13	7.86
4	7.73	14	7.23
5	8.44	15	7.33
6	7.50	16	7.30
7	8.28	17	7.67
8	7.62	18	6.90
9	8.33	19	7.38
10	7.60	20	7.44

Plot the data on a cumulative sum chart, using any suitable type of chart with the appropriate correction values and decision procedures.

What are the average run lengths at μ_0 and μ_1 for your chosen decision procedure?

57 A cusum scheme is to be installed to monitor gas consumption in a chemical plant where a heat treatment is an integral part of the process. The QC engineers know from intensive studies that when the system is operating as it was designed the average amount of gas required in a period of eight hours would be 250 therms, with a standard deviation of 25 therms.

The following table shows the gas consumption and shift length for 20 shifts recently.

Shift no.	Hours operation (H)	Gas consumption (G)
1	8	256
2	4	119
3	8	278
4	4	122
5	6	215
6	6	170
7	8	262
8	8	216
9	3	103
10	8	206
11	3	83
12	8	214
13	3	95
14	8	234
15	8	266
16	4	150
17	8	284
18	3	118
19	8	298
20	4	138

Standardize the gas consumption to an eight-hour shift length i.e. standardized gas consumption X is given by

$$X = \left(\frac{G}{H}\right) \times 8$$

Using a reference value of 250 hours construct a cumulative sum chart based on X. Apply a selected V-mask after each point is plotted.

When you identify a significant change state when the change occurred, and start the cusum chart again with the same reference value of 250 therms assuming that appropriate corrective action has been taken.

Appendix J

Further Reading

BESTERFIELD, D.H., 1979, *Quality Control,* Prentice-Hall Inc., New Jersey.

BRITISH STANDARDS INSTITUTION, 1981, Handbook 22, *Quality Assurance*, 1985, Handbook 24, *Quality Control*, BSI: London.

CAPLEN, R.H., 1982 (4th Edition), *Practical Approach to Quality Control*, Business Books, London.

CROSBY, P.B., 1979, *Quality is Free*, 1985, *Quality without Tears*, McGraw-Hill: New York.

DAVIES, O.L. and GOLDSMITH, P.L. (Editors), 1972 (4th Edition), *Statistical Methods in Research and Production*, Oliver and Boyd (for ICI), Edinburgh.

DUNCAN, A.J., 1974, *Quality Control and Industrial Statistics*, Richard D. Irwin, Illinois.

FEIGENBAUM, A.V., 1983 (3rd Edition), *Total Quality Control*, McGraw-Hill: New York.

GRANT, E.L. and LEAVENWORTH, R.S., 1980, *Statistical Quality Control*, McGraw-Hill, New York.

INSTITUTE OF QUALITY ASSURANCE, 1975, *A Guide to Process Capability Studies*, IQA, London.

ISHIKAWA, K., 1982, *Guide to Quality Control*, Asian Productivity Association, Tokyo.

JAMIESON, A., 1982, *Introduction to Quality Control*, Reston, A. Prentice-Hall Co.

JURAN, J.M. (Editor) 1975, (3rd Edition), *Quality Control Handbook*, McGraw-Hill, New York.

JURAN, J.M. and GRYNA, F.M., 1980 (2nd Edition), *Quality Planning and Analysis*, McGraw-Hill: New York.

MORONEY, M.J., 1978 (2nd Edition), *Facts from Figures*, Penguin, Harmondsworth.

MURDOCH, J., 1979, *Control Charts*, MacMillan, London.

MURDOCH, J. and BARNES, J.A., 1975, *Statistical Tables for Science, Engineering, Management and Business Studies*, MacMillan, London.

OTT, E.R., 1975, *Process Quality Control – Troubleshooting and Interpretation of data*, McGraw-Hill, Kogakusha, New York.

PRICE, F., 1984, *Right First Time*, Gower: London.

WETHERILL, G.B., 1977, *Sampling Inspection and Q.C.*, Science Paperbacks, London, Chapman & Hall.

Index